1866-1991

125th

ANNIVERSARY

WHAT
COUNTS

A JOHN MACRAE BOOK

HENRY HOLT AND COMPANY   NEW YORK

~~~ WHAT ~~~
COUNTS

THE COMPLETE HARPER'S INDEX

EDITED BY
CHARIS CONN AND ILENA SILVERMAN
AND THE STAFF OF *HARPER'S MAGAZINE*
ASSOCIATE EDITOR: PAUL TOUGH
WITH A FOREWORD BY
LEWIS H. LAPHAM

Library of Congress Cataloging-in-Publication Data
What counts : the complete Harper's index / edited by Charis Conn &
Ilena Silverman ; associate editor, Paul Tough, with a foreword
by Lewis H. Lapham.
            p.   cm.
        "A John Macrae book."
    ISBN 0-8050-1279-6.—ISBN 0-8050-1895-6 (pbk.)
1. Handbooks, vade-mecums, etc.   2. Statistics.   I. Conn, Charis.
II. Silverman, Ilena.   III. Tough, Paul.   IV. Harper's magazine.
AG105.W5   1991   91-793
031.02—dc20   CIP

Designed by Claire Vaccaro

ACKNOWLEDGMENTS

Almost by definition, a collection such as this one relies on many dedicated people and much cooperation. And we have been fortunate, over the past year, to have had the advantages of both. From the beginning, the most daunting aspect of this book was organization, and we were lucky early on to encounter Manny Howard, the person most responsible for helping to keep these thousands of bits of information in some order throughout the updating process. Manny headed our research team, keeping tabs on the facts and their accuracy, and often contributing lively alternatives, many of which appear throughout these pages. He was aided by a small army of fact-checkers, all of whom worked with the creative tenacity such a project requires. The newcomers who had never worked at *Harper's* before—Suzanna Ashton, Lauren Goldstein, and Heather Despres-Burack—were quick to embrace and devour the task set before them. And the old hands—current and former *Harper's Magazine* interns—performed, as usual, above and beyond the call of duty. They are: Scott Anderson, Jennifer Barton, Sarah Burns, Matthew Butcher, Noah Green, Randi Rose, and Alexandra Tager. In addition, special thanks go to Henry Sidel, who did a thoughtful and meticulous job of checking all the sources.

ACKNOWLEDGMENTS

The *Harper's* Index is a truly collaborative effort, and the material in this book owes its essential energy and wit to every member of the magazine's staff, including Colin Harrison, Jack Hitt, Lewis Lapham, Gerald Marzorati, Elliott Rabin, Ellen Rosenbush, Deborah Rust, and Ann Stern. In addition, special recognition must go to Paul Tough, a *Harper's* editor, and our associate editor on this project, who has been intimately connected with the Index for years and has provided many of its most creative ideas and intrepid research. His sharp intellect and editing skills along with his technical wizardry have been invaluable. Michael Pollan, *Harper's* executive editor, has edited the Index since its inception and has been the guiding force behind its evolution. He brought to this book's pages the same incisive editorial judgment he has given the monthly Index for the last seven years. Jeanne Dubi, *Harper's* general manager, provided tremendous assistance when it came to budgets and planning, and Rick MacArthur, the magazine's publisher, gave his invaluable support throughout this project.

Special thanks also go to Paul Horwitz and Alan Burdick, both friends of the magazine, who have played an important part in the Index as well as in this book; and to former editor Eric Etheridge, whose years of work on the Index have enriched this collection. Finally, we want to thank all of the magazine's seven years' worth of editorial interns—sixty-one in all—who have done extraordinary work on the Index as well as on the magazine as a whole. This book is dedicated to them.

CONTENTS

CONTENTS

CONTENTS

CONTENTS

FOREWORD: BY THE NUMBERS

The age of faith counted the number of angels who danced on the head of a pin. The age of reason counts the hours of television watched in American households or the cost of renting the *Queen Elizabeth II* for an overnight "cruise to nowhere." The next century presumably will count something else—ants or krill or grains of sand—because the belief in statistics is as stubborn as the wish to arrange the universe in a pattern adjusted to one's own sleeve length or hat size.

Among all the world's peoples, none assign as much weight to numbers as do the Americans. We arrive from so many points of mixed origin that we never quite learn to speak one another's languages, and so we agree, for lack of a common folktale, on the vocabulary of numbers. Fortunately for all concerned, numbers can be made to tell as many stories as a crooked lawyer or an old comedian. Dressed up in the proper context and placed in the appropriate column, a statistic or a percentage point counts as a closing argument, a proof of virtue or a judgment of heaven.

The *Harper's* Index sets numbers to the task of taking

soundings. I hit upon the device, which is that of an Arabic algorithm, on an otherwise unmathematical afternoon in the autumn of 1983 when I was in the midst of redrafting *Harper's Magazine* to fit the specifications of a new audience and a revised purpose. By 1983 the forms and uses of journalism were changing as rapidly as the foreign exchange rate. The emphasis had shifted from the investigative to the interpretive aspects of the trade. No longer was it a matter of discovering the secret that nobody knew—the name of the general's mistress or the whereabouts of the Bermuda Triangle—but rather the art of placing the news that everybody knew into some kind of intelligible sequence. The more urgent stories of the day—the dynamics of revolution in the Third World, say, or the likelihood of collapse in the international banking system—required a drawing together of elements increasingly diffuse.

The problem was the surfeit of information. Too much news in too many denominations (technical, historical, theoretical, statistical, and existential) was arriving from too many directions. How then to assemble the bewildering fragments of evidence into a coherent argument or design?

The environmentalists long ago learned to speak of ecosystems as the long chains of causation that sustain the balances of power among the organisms of the natural world. Analogous and equally subtle lines of connection run through the cultural and political provinces of experience, binding together the economies of nations and the gravitational fields of human thought. Most people know, instinctively if not because of what they were taught at school, that the lines exist, that all the pieces of reality fit somehow together in patterns variously identified as chemistry, Marxism, or God. If the lines become hard to see in a world more accurately represented by the randomness of quantum mechanics than by Newton's geometry, then they must be brought into focus by acts of the imagination.

Approached from the perspective of a magazine editor, the problems of interpretation (i.e., how to make the lines of connection visible in the light of print) prompted the invention of new editorial forms. Of those introduced to *Harper's Magazine* in the winter of 1984 (among them the Readings, the Annotation, and the Forum) the one that delighted me the most was the *Harper's* Index. It was the one that attempted a rule of numbers, and I took as much of an old and superstitious pleasure in it as I imagine the Aztecs discovered in their stone calendars or the ancient Chinese in the throwing of the *I Ching*.

Every month *Harper's Magazine* publishes the Index as a single page of numbers that measure, in one way or another, the drifting tide of events. The list might note the number of people on the waiting list to see an execution in Florida (100), the price paid at auction for a 1909 Honus Wagner baseball card ($451,000), the average weight of a male bear in Alaska (1,000 pounds) and in Pennsylvania (325 pounds), or the number of New York City police officers who belong to the Screen Actors Guild (350). Taken separately or together, or sometimes in juxtaposition (e.g., "Amount the Reagan administration budgeted for military bands in 1987: $154,200,000/Amount it budgeted for the National Endowment for the Arts: $144,900,000"), the month's representative numbers form a kind of plumb line cast into the infinite sea of number and event. In no way definitive, the Index speaks to the wonder of the world's density, contradiction, and desire.

Since its inception, the Index has attracted a large and friendly crowd of readers who accept its premises and laugh at its jokes. It was perhaps the most radical of the new journalistic forms introduced seven years ago as part of the magazine's new design, and it is now reprinted, in whole or in part, by eighteen American newspapers as well as by newspapers and magazines in Germany, Italy, Spain, France, Portugal, Greece, and Japan. Some of the less controversial numbers—"Life span of a baseball in a major-league game (in pitches): 7"—have made guest appearances on network television.

e.e. cummings once defined poetry as the art of "asking the more beautiful question," and as often as not the Index numbers serve as metaphors, acquiring literary value by reason of the questions they ask or the images they retrieve from the abyss. Perceived as a collection of notes and sketches or, more fancifully, as an anthology of very brief tales, the Index accommodates itself to as many interpretations as can be constructed by the English Department at Yale. The compiling of the present volume delighted its editors with a sense of discovery, and

FOREWORD

we hope that the reader also will take pleasure in the stories that numbers, properly instructed, can be made to tell.

Lewis H. Lapham
1991

INTRODUCTION

To most people, the prospect of reading a book composed entirely of statistics is about as appealing as taking a standardized test. Statistics have traditionally been regarded as dry, humorless informational nuggets, and as such have been treated as little more than efficient tools for reducing a complex situation to a few manageable digits. Viewed in this way, statistics are merely one-dimensional—incapable of capturing the richness and subtlety of history or everyday life.

But as we all know from years of watching "Dragnet," facts—numerical or otherwise—need not be isolated from larger truths. Whenever Sergeant Joe Friday would demand, "Just the facts, ma'am," he was asking for a detailed, impartial account of events, free from analysis or interpretation. Yet each week his simple request invariably led to a story—one filled with characters, landscapes, and a plethora of intangibles—that somehow added up to much more than just a collection of facts. Similarly, a carefully chosen statistic, or a collection of them deliberately organized, can go a long way toward capturing the stories of our lives and times.

INTRODUCTION

If at first glance these pages present facts, then a closer look will reveal something more—narratives, commentaries, even jokes. In assembling the most compelling statistics from the first seven years of the *Harper's Index*, we have created eighty-one rubrics, or mini-indexes, which touch on such themes as marriage, weather, crime, high finance, and sex. Each rubric provides a numerical snapshot of a political, social, or cultural phenomenon. The eighty-one indexes are collected under ten broad headings—Civics, Social Studies, History, Geography, Communications, Economics, Science, Psychology, Home Ec, and Vacation. These categories roughly mirror the standard American high-school curriculum, and so represent a familiar, if not entirely comprehensive, way of classifying the world's information.

In addition to offering a collection of colorful snapshots, this book can be used as a reference work that provides a compendium of quantitative information. Much as one might turn to *Bartlett's Familiar Quotations* in search of the perfect epigram, the reader of this collection will find statistics to suit any occasion. In addition to the ten headings in the table of contents, an index beginning on page 275 will help the reader locate information about such specific, far-flung subjects as Richard Nixon, murder, sunglasses, gambling, Elvis, and dolphins. When the moment demands the authoritative weight of a statistic—to punctuate a speech, a toast, or a professional presentation, or merely to settle a family argument—this book provides assistance.

The most commonly asked question about the Index is: How do you get your numbers? The short answer is: any way we can. Here is the long one:

Each month staffers pore through hundreds of magazines, newspapers, newsletters, and reports. In addition, every member of the *Harper's* staff has developed the habit of "Indexthink"—the ability (almost a Pavlovian response for all of us now) to see the world through Index-tinted glasses. Whether we are reading for pleasure, watching the TV news, or simply listening to the radio before work in the morning, we are ever alert to all things numerical. The clippings and scribbled notes that document what we've read and heard each month fill a large wire basket from which the best statistics are later culled.

Indexthink also involves seeing numbers between the lines, figuring out how to describe a trend or news story in an original, quantitative way. Many of the ideas for the Index are generated at a monthly staff meeting, where the talk can run from Soviet politics to organic gardening to rock music. At an Index meeting held during congressional debates on the Persian Gulf War in early 1991, an editor wondered aloud how many members of Congress might be personally affected by such a war. After some discussion, we decided to find out how many members had children serving in the region. (A week later, after extensive research, we found our answer: 7.)

During a meeting held in 1989, an editor who had recently watched the final episodes of "Miami Vice" and "Family Ties" remarked that the passing of these popular, quintessentially eighties shows deserved some notice. On rescreening them, we realized that a simple enumeration of each episode's most basic elements might neatly sum up their overall flavor and appeal. Our research intern dutifully employed a "clicker," a hardware-store counting device we've used many times, and came up with this:

Number of hugs in the final episode of "Family Ties": 20

Number of shootings in the final episode of "Miami Vice": 40

The ideas from our meetings—our hunches about numbers to look for—coupled with all of the clippings and notes on the numbers we have already found, form the basis of each month's list. The Index, however, is more than simply a random collection of pithy numbers. Every statistic in a given month's Index is related in one way or another to the number immediately preceding and following it, and the reader is encouraged to draw meaning from each juxtaposition. In some cases the first line plays straight man for the second, as in this pair published at the height of the U.S. government's war on drug harvests in South America:

Percentage of Peru's annual coca crop destroyed by U.S.-assisted forces in 1989: 1

Percentage destroyed by insects: 20

Some connections are more subtle than others:

Number of employees on the congressional payroll who are relatives of representatives or senators: 74

Number of leeches sold each year to American surgeons and hospitals by Leeches USA of Westbury, New York: 10,000

This last duo is not in the text of this book. The leech number remains onstage alone, without the foil of congressional nepotism. The study that produced the congressional figure was newly finished when we cited it in a 1988 issue of *Harper's*, but this research has not, to our knowledge, been repeated. This is just one of many statistics that did not survive the yearlong updating process for this book. Attempting to verify each month's Index has taught us that for every three numbers that stand up to scrutiny, one crumbles during the fact-checking process. Sometimes numbers fail for simple reasons: A publication makes a typographical error or a reporter under deadline makes a mistake. More often, we must abandon a number because we are unable to prove its veracity.

In a classic example, one of our country's best daily newspapers printed an article in 1990 datelined Warsaw, which mentioned that 70,000 Poles had turned in their license plates because they could no longer afford to keep their cars. Since the article did not cite a source, we tried to confirm the information independently. The Polish government—stymied perhaps by the language barrier—was no help. Calls to the Polish News Agency and a number of Polish publications were equally unfruitful; many said they had heard this statistic, but no one could cite a source. In frustration we contacted the American reporter, assuming he had an anonymous source of his own. To our dismay, he conceded that he had gotten the 70,000 figure from his translator, who had heard it on the local Polish radio news, and that he could not vouch for its accuracy.

Books are also often guilty of providing information without verifying its accuracy. In a recent collection of environmental trivia, we came across the intriguing formulation that without electricity and other modern energy sources the average American would require 500 human slaves to maintain his or her life-style. Unlike many authors we have encountered, this writer actually kept a file of his sources. As often happens, his source turned out to be another book—published six years earlier. Though this information was no doubt dated, we assumed that whatever equation the original book's author had employed could be updated according to the most recent data on energy consumption. But to find the original equation, we had to find the original author, which took some doing. The book's publisher had no idea how to contact him, but referred us to the university listed in the author's bio, which in turn told us that he had retired years earlier. Our resourceful intern finally found the man at home and asked him how he had come up with such a startling statistic. He did not remember. "I'm eighty-one years old and I wrote that book ten years ago," he explained. His one vague memory of how he might have arrived at such a number was this: He said he might have read it in a book.

When our research interns are not trying to confirm numbers that have been published or broadcast, they are conducting what we refer to in the source section of this book as "*Harper's* research." This research runs the gamut from tallying hugs and murders during TV shows to counting exclamation points in Tom Wolfe's *Bonfire of the Vanities*.

In their intrepid search for information, interns have also had lively discussions with celebrities ranging from Henny Youngman to Jay McInerney. In 1989, McInerney helped us to pinpoint a fact about his first novel that close reading alone could not adequately determine:

Lines of coke done in the book *Bright Lights, Big City*: 48

Our interns' brushes with fame have become the source of much office lore. One of our favorite fact-checking episodes occurred in the fall of 1990 when an ambitious intern sought to determine the total number of jokes in Milton Berle's voluminous collection. The intern jotted down the following dialogue minutes after ending his phone conversation with Mr. Berle, who was reached at the Friars Club in Los Angeles:

"Hello, Mr. Berle, I'm calling from *Harper's Magazine*. Are you familiar with *Harper's*?"

"Yeah, sure, you think I don't know *Harper's*? What do you want?"

"Well, I was wondering if you could help me with some information we're trying to compile for our Index."

"Like what?"

"Well, I'd like to know the number of jokes you own."

"The number of jokes? What do you mean? What's this for?"

"For our list of statistics."

"So what do you want, a number?"

"Yes, like the number of file cabinets, maybe."

"Yeah, well I keep them all on computer."

"Well, do you know how many you have?"

"The number? Sure, six and a half million."

"Six and a half million?"

"Yeah, sure. What? You don't believe me? I very graciously answer the phone and you're giving me a hard time?"

"No, no. It's just that that's a lot of jokes—six and a half million."

"Well, that's the fuckin' number."

"Okay, okay. Thank you, Mr. Berle. Thanks for your time."

"Right. G'bye."

Although we heard it straight from the horse's mouth, this number was too incredible to take on faith. It was never published.

Not every fact-checking experience is as brief as this one. A more typical research effort requires numerous phone calls and close scrutiny of long, often impenetrable reports and documents. During this process an intern becomes an apprentice expert in the subject at hand—

interviewing several authoritative sources, picking apart and comparing their definitions, and questioning their assumptions. Often, after days of checking, it becomes clear that the situation we are trying to quantify is so complicated that it cannot adequately be explained in a single line, and we must abandon it. It is a difficult and often frustrating process, but we have found that it is the best way to insure that our numbers are credible.

"There are three kinds of lies," wrote Mark Twain in 1924, quoting Disraeli, "—lies, damn lies, and statistics." This is a claim we do not shy away from. Although we deal in numbers, we are by no means convinced of their intrinsic reliability. We know as well as anyone that numbers can be used to manipulate truth. And the healthy skepticism that informs all our research has stood us in good stead. For after wading through the seductive statistics bandied about on the evening news and in the morning paper, we often come upon the thing that makes it all worthwhile: something pure that can be lifted up to the light and seen for what it is—a single number that tells a true story succinctly and powerfully. We know that truth is elusive, but we hope that by stripping down reality to its more solid components, the Index—and this book—will provide a few sturdy, inviting footholds in the slippery mountains of information we all encounter daily.

—Charis Conn and Ilena Silverman
1991

CIVICS

School Days

Higher Education

Voters and Voting

The Campaign Trail

The Congress

The White House

The Courts

Fines

Crime

Punishment

The Drug War

Secrecy

SCHOOL DAYS

Ratio of the average salary of an American CEO to that of an American public-school teacher in 1960: **38:1**

Ratio today: **73:1**

Percentage of new American public-school teachers who say they plan to quit the profession within five years: **34**

Amount Cleveland public-high-school students receive toward college tuition for every A grade they earn in an academic course: **$40**

Portion of American high-school seniors who cannot locate Latin America on a world map: **1/3**

Number of states that have raised high-school graduation requirements since 1980: **33**

Number of hours that an American teenager spends each week in class or studying: **38**

Number of hours that a Soviet teenager spends: **52**

Number that a Japanese teenager spends: **59**

Number of Japanese children who have died since 1985 as a result of disciplinary beatings by school personnel: **5**

WHAT COUNTS

Number of New York City public-school teachers who were assaulted on the job in 1989: **710**

Percentage of American teachers who said in 1966 that if they could start over, they probably would not teach: **11**

Percentage who said this in 1986: **31**

Percentage of Americans who say that a schoolteacher "is worth at least as much as a member of Congress": **72**

Average ratio of students to teachers in a U.S. public-school classroom in 1955: **27:1**

Average ratio of students to teachers today: **17:1**

Number of U.S. states that claim test scores in their elementary schools are above the national average: **50**

Estimated number of American children who are currently schooled at home: **375,000**

Percentage of private-school students in New York City who are not white: **16**

Percentage of public-school students in New York City who are white: **20**

Percentage of adults who say they are against sex education in public schools: **10**

Number of the 29 states requiring AIDS education in public schools that require that abstinence be stressed: **18**

Number of these states that also require discussion of condom use: **3**

CIVICS

Average number of points a student gains on the math section of the SAT per thirty hours of preparatory classes: **25**

Estimated number of private college consultants for high-school students in the United States: **450**

Percentage increase, since 1973, in the number of three- and four-year-olds attending U.S. nursery schools: **92**

Number of one-year-olds on the waiting list for the French for Tots program in New York City: **152**

HIGHER EDUCATION

Rank of national and local Miss America pageants among all sources of college scholarship money for women: **1**

Percentage of U.S. colleges that do not require an American history course for graduation: **80**

Percentage decrease, since 1979, in the number of American studies professorships in Britain: **50**

Estimated ratio of engineers to lawyers graduated each year in the United States: **1:50**

Estimated ratio in Japan: **10:1**

Percentage of doctoral degrees conferred by U.S. engineering schools that are earned by foreigners: **55**

Portion of the 1990 freshman class at MIT that was Asian-American: **1/4**

Amount spent by the University of Alabama in the 1989–90 academic year on its physics department: **$1,300,000**

Amount spent on athletics: **$8,600,000**

Percentage of recruited student athletes at Division I NCAA universities who graduate: **47**

Percentage of all students at Division I NCAA universities who graduate: **47**

Percentage of 1971 Yale Law School graduates who took jobs in the public sector: **23**

Percentage of 1990 graduates who did: **8**

Tons of gold made into class rings in the United States each year: **7.5**

Number of honorary degrees held by Sammy Davis, Jr.: **4**

Portion of Harvard students who graduate with honors: **4/5**

Percentage of college students who agree with the statement, "The higher the tuition, the better the education": **27**

Number of people who graduated from Dale Carnegie courses in the 1980s: **1,320,000**

Percentage of male college students who say they might commit rape if there was no chance of being caught: **35**

Percentage of male college students who say that "some women look as though they're just asking to be raped": **84**

Number of U.S. universities that have instituted restrictions on public speech since 1988: **137**

Chances that a student will develop nearsightedness while in college: **1 in 3**

Number of the 6 best-selling extracurricular books in college bookstores in 1990 that were collections of cartoons: **4**

Number of U.S. universities that have a Taco Bell Distinguished Professorship of Fast Service: **1**

Number of nanny schools in the United States: **18**

Number of butler schools: **1**

Amount an unemployed graduate student sought in a consumer-fraud suit against Goddard College, the student's alma mater, in 1989: **$61,500**

Percentage of students at the Dunkin' Donuts Training Center who do not pass the six-week training course: **8**

VOTERS AND VOTING

Median age of an American voter: **45**

Chances that a college-educated American who did not vote will claim to have done so: **1 in 2**

Chances that a high-school dropout who did not vote will claim to have done so: **1 in 5**

Estimated number of names on U.S. voter-registration rolls that represent people who have either died or moved: **20,000,000**

Number of states that have voted Democratic in every presidential election since 1968: **0**

Number of presidential elections since 1964 in which the Democratic candidate won a majority of the white vote: **0**

Chances that a Republican in 1955 was a white Southerner: **1 in 10**

Chances in 1988: **1 in 4**

Number of states in which the percentage of blacks who are registered to vote equals or exceeds the percentage of whites who are: **16**

Percentage of all Los Angelenos who voted for Mayor Bradley in the 1989 election, which he won: **5**

Percentage of black voters in 1988 who considered George Bush the "craziest" candidate: **13**

Percentage of voters who had an unfavorable opinion of George Bush four months before the 1988 presidential election: **40**

Percentage of voters who had an unfavorable opinion of Walter Mondale four months before the 1984 presidential election: **29**

Percentage of Americans who say they would vote for an atheist for president: **31**

Percentage who say they would vote for a homosexual: **26**

Number of write-in votes in the 1985 Boise, Idaho, mayoral election for Mr. Potato Head: **4**

THE CAMPAIGN TRAIL

Number of the last 10 presidential elections that were won by the taller candidate: **8**

Number that were won by the nominee who gave the more optimistic convention acceptance speech: **9**

Total campaign funds spent for each vote cast in the 1988 presidential election: **$5.46**

Percentage change, between the 1984 and 1988 presidential elections, in funds raised by the Democratic party: **+38**

Percentage change in funds raised by the Republican party: **−10**

Change, since 1980, in the total amount Americans checked off on tax returns each year for the Presidential Campaign Fund: **−$8,500,000**

Number of Democratic officeholders who have become Republicans since the 1988 presidential election: **241**

Estimated number of times George Bush recited the Pledge of

Allegiance in the month following his 1988 presidential nomination: **25**

Number of times George Bush recited the Pledge of Allegiance while a student at Greenwich Country Day School: **0**

Number of times the word *Christian* appeared in Pat Robertson's 1988 presidential campaign brochure: **0**

Number of the 3 exclusive clubs from which Lloyd Bentsen resigned during the 1988 presidential campaign that he has since rejoined: **3**

Percentage of the top sixty Republican campaign aides during the 1988 presidential election who were white males: **87**

Percentage who were black or Hispanic: **0**

Percentage of contributors to Jesse Jackson's 1988 presidential campaign who gave five hundred dollars or more: **12**

Percentage of contributors to George Bush's 1988 campaign who gave five hundred dollars or more: **78**

Average amount of campaign funds received by Senator Lloyd Bentsen in 1987, per day: **$12,744**

Funds budgeted by the Republican National Committee for negative research on Michael Dukakis during the 1988 presidential campaign: **$500,000**

Funds budgeted by the Democratic National Committee for negative research on George Bush during the 1988 presidential campaign: **$250,000**

Amount a cochairman of the Bush campaign's finance committee contributed to the Dukakis campaign: **$1,000**

CIVICS

Number of jokes told about the Democratic presidential candidates on late-night network television in January and February of 1988: **110**

Number of jokes told about the Republican candidates: **173**

Amount the Republican party raised during the 1980s for every dollar raised by the Democratic party: **$3.46**

Number of Democratic presidential candidates since 1932 who received the majority of endorsements from U.S. daily newspapers: **1**

Percentage of GOP state chairmen who say that Dan Quayle should not run for vice-president in 1992: **27**

Number of the 31 congressional candidates that President Bush campaigned for in 1990 who lost: **23**

Total contributions to 1988 congressional candidates that came from PACs formed by foreign companies: **$2,800,000**

Size of the campaign contribution for which Arizona senator Dennis DeConcini says he "would literally go any place": **$10,000**

Number of Democratic National Committee staffers during the 1988 presidential campaign whose job title was Press Office Liaison to Celebrities: **1**

Amount that comedian Pat Paulsen has raised for his 1992 presidential campaign: **$37**

THE CONGRESS

Percentage of members of Congress who say that "virtuous living is the path to salvation": **39**

Rank of the Tobacco Institute, among the groups that paid members of Congress the most in honoraria in 1988: **1**

Total leftover campaign funds that members of the 101st Congress can legally keep if they retire or lose their seats by 1992: **$42,000,000**

Total number of roll-call votes missed by members of the U.S. Congress in 1989: **9,500**

Percentage of congressional roll-call votes between 1981 and 1989 in which legislation supported by the president was rejected: **38**

Percentage of congressional roll-call votes since 1989 in which legislation supported by the president was rejected: **53**

Portion of all bills passed by Congress in 1990 that established commemorative days, weeks, or months: **1/10**

Number of minutes Congress spent in October 1990 debating the administration's request for new S&L bailout funds: **23**

Number of minutes spent debating a proposal to renovate the Capitol hairdressing salon: **40**

Funding Congress proposed in 1990 for the Institute of Decision Making in Cedar Falls, Iowa: **$1,000,000**

Percentage of Americans who say "a good car mechanic is worth as much as a member of Congress": **21**

Percentage of Americans who say the group with too little influence in government is people like themselves: **91**

Number of child-care bills introduced during the 1979–80 session of Congress: **93**

Number introduced during the 1989–90 session: **214**

Percentage of Republican congresswomen who are prochoice: **66**

Maximum number of times a senator's name is allowed to appear on each page of his or her constituent newsletter: **8**

Percentage change, since 1978, in the amount of videotape used by members of Congress in the House TV studio: **+300**

Takes required to film former House speaker Tip O'Neill's 1987 Miller Lite commercial: **79**

Number of minutes of *Die Hard 2* watched in 1990 by a congressional subcommittee researching computer terrorism: **5**

Number of times the phrase *do the right thing* was used during congressional debates in the six months after Spike Lee's film was released: **67**

Number of those times it was used in reference to racial issues: **1**

Number of times it was used in reference to a congressional pay raise: **16**

THE WHITE HOUSE

Number of years by which an American president is likely to fall short of his life expectancy: **3**

Rank of Abraham Lincoln among the U.S. presidents most often portrayed in films: **1**

Estimated number of times that a U.S. president has sent troops into combat situations without a congressional declaration of war: **125**

Number of years, since 1953, in which a president has lost more congressional votes than he has won: **2**

Number of these years that occurred during the Reagan administration: **2**

Percentage of presidential appointees who say they have trouble understanding financial disclosure forms: **70**

Average number of Americans who watched the Senate Watergate hearings each day that they were broadcast on television in 1973: **1,000,000**

Percentage of Americans who said in 1973 that they had "a great deal of confidence in the executive branch of government": **19**

Percentage who said this in 1989: **17**

Percentage of Americans in 1985 who couldn't recognize George Bush: **44**

Percentage who couldn't recognize Mr. Clean: **7**

Rank of Mr. Rogers, among preschoolers' first choice for president of the United States: **1**

Rank of George Bush, Dan Quayle, and Marion Barry, among the most common butts of jokes on late-night network TV talk shows in 1990: **1, 2, 3**

Percentage of Americans who said in September 1988 that they didn't know enough about Dan Quayle to form an opinion: **25**

Percentage of Americans who said this one year later: **45**

Number of times that Dan Quayle has accidentally hit the Secret Service emergency button under his desk at the White House: **3**

Percentage of American adults who say they would like to be president: **11**

Percentage who say they would like their child to be president: **41**

Percentage of preschool children who say that if they were president they would eat ice cream for every meal: **21**

THE COURTS

Per capita cost of the U.S. justice system in 1985: **$191**

Per capita cost today: **$248**

Percentage of federal district judges appointed by Ronald Reagan who are millionaires: **25**

Percentage who graduated from Ivy League schools: **15**

Average age of federal judges appointed by President Reagan: **49**

Chances that a sitting federal judge was appointed by Ronald Reagan or George Bush: **1 in 2**

Percentage increase in wiretaps authorized by federal judges since 1980: **280**

Estimated amount the Justice Department has spent to prosecute the Iran-Contra case: **$20,500,000**

Amount the four defendants allegedly diverted to the Contras: **$3,800,000**

Amount a federal legal-aid program spent in 1989 on a legal brief arguing that the program itself was unconstitutional: **$77,000**

Number of states in which parolees and probationers can be required to help pay for their own supervision: **22**

Average number of days it takes to try and sentence a defendant to death in Ohio: **22**

Average number of days it takes in Georgia: **3**

Federal and state laws declared unconstitutional by the Warren Court between 1953 and 1969: **130**

Federal and state laws declared unconstitutional by the Burger Court between 1969 and 1986: **326**

Percentage increase, since 1959, in the number of Supreme Court cases that involve the separation of powers: **244**

Portion of the Supreme Court opinions in 1989 that were decided by a five-to-four vote: **1/4**

Number of expert witnesses listed in the *Lawyer's Desk Reference* in 1970: **500**

Number listed today: **5,000**

Percentage of lawyers who advertise: **25**

Average number of attorneys who are disbarred in the United States each year: **340**

Portion of the $25 billion awarded each year in liability lawsuits that goes to attorneys: **1/3**

Chances that a resident of Washington, D.C., is a lawyer: **1 in 10**

Total amount two New York lawyers were fined for having a fistfight during a deposition in 1989: **$11,000**

Jail sentence a Tucson judge gave a lawyer in 1988 for wearing green sneakers in his courtroom, in hours: **40**

World's record for the most footnotes in a law review article: **4,824**

Number of legal articles Supreme Court Justice David Souter has ever published: **1**

Number of the 145 nominations to the Supreme Court since 1789 that were not confirmed: **29**

Number of the four Supreme Court nominations made by Millard Fillmore that were not confirmed: **3**

Number of Supreme Court judges in 1984 who voted against legalizing the recording of TV broadcasts by VCR: **4**

Percentage of Americans who can correctly name the chief justice of the Supreme Court: **9**

Percentage of Americans who can correctly name the judge on "The People's Court": **54**

Ratio of the number of decisions handed down by the Supreme Court to the number handed down by Judge Wapner, since 1980: **2:3**

FINES

Total amount convicted drug traffickers in the United States owe in criminal fines: **$108,000,000**

Total amount New York City drivers owe in parking fines: **$461,000,000**

CIVICS

Number of parking tickets issued to the Soviet Mission to the United Nations in 1989: **7,612**

Average fine in Bavaria, Germany, for calling a traffic officer a *dämlischer Bulle* (stupid bull): **$1,710**

Average fine for calling a traffic officer a *Stinkstiefel* (smelly boot): **$51**

Fine that a German legislator must pay for missing a roll-call vote: **$40**

Fine proposed by a Tennessee state representative in 1989 for assaulting anyone desecrating a U.S. or state flag: **$1**

Fine for parking a pickup truck in one's own driveway in Flossmoor, Illinois: **$10**

Maximum amount a Los Angeles taxi company can be fined if its drivers are found wearing anything plaid: **$1,500**

Amount Ravalli County, Montana, fined itself after one of its trucks was found to have exceeded the legal load limit: **$350**

Amount the county paid local attorneys to prosecute and defend itself: **$1,175**

Minimum fine for carrying dummy passengers in car-pool lanes on Virginia highways: **$50**

Fine for selling or eating dog meat in Manila: **$100**

Fine for selling or eating dog meat in California: **$1,000**

Maximum fine for performing an animal sacrifice in Los Angeles: **$1,000**

Maximum fine for urinating in an elevator in Singapore: **$500**

CRIME

Chances that a burglary in the United States will be solved: **1 in 7**

Portion of all robberies in which the victim and the assailant are of the same race: **2/3**

Portion of all violent crimes in which the victim knows the attacker: **2/5**

Chances that an American woman will be the victim of a rape or an attempted rape in her lifetime: **1 in 12**

Ratio of the number of rapes reported by women with annual incomes of less than three thousand dollars to the number of rapes reported by those with incomes of more than fifteen thousand dollars: **6:1**

Rank of the District of Columbia, Nevada, and Alaska, among states in which a woman's chances of being murdered are the highest: **1, 2, 3**

Chances that a murderer will never appear in a courtroom: **1 in 3**

Chances that the victim of a violent crime is under the age of twenty: **1 in 3**

Percentage of American households in the West in which a member has been the victim of a violent crime: **6.2**

Percentage in the Northeast: **3.6**

Percentage increase in Atlantic City's crime rate since gambling was legalized there in 1977: **150**

Average amount stolen by a bank robber, per incident: **$3,000**

Average amount stolen each year by a supermarket employee who steals: **$1,209**

Average amount stolen by a shoplifter, in value of merchandise, per incident: **$40**

Percentage increase, since 1986, in the number of federal convictions for money laundering: **267**

Value of the bootleg music recordings seized in the United States in 1990: **$43,000,000**

Estimated number of forgeries discovered since 1980 in the collection of New York's Metropolitan Museum of Art: **50**

Estimated number of pirate attacks on ships at sea since 1984: **138**

Estimated number of weather vanes reported stolen in New England in 1990: **200**

Number of armed robberies in Iceland in 1990: **0**

PUNISHMENT

Rank of the prison system, among the fastest-growing sectors of U.S. government employment: **1**

WHAT COUNTS

Percentage increase, since 1985, in the number of privately operated correctional facilities in the United States: **633**

Average weekly increase, in 1989, in the population of state and federal prisons: **1,800**

Chances that an American man has spent a night in jail: **1 in 5**

Number of states that allow prisoners to have conjugal visits: **8**

Average age at which an inmate in a state prison first had sex: **14**

Percentage increase in the number of women in U.S. prisons since 1974: **359**

Number of the 121 U.S. death-row inmates executed since 1977 whose victims were white: **101**

Percentage of U.S. prison inmates in 1926 who were black: **23**

Percentage of U.S. prison inmates in 1989 who were black: **47**

Rank of South Africa and the United States, among countries with the highest per capita prison population in 1979: **1, 2**

Rank today: **2, 1**

Average number of South African police officers who resigned each day in 1990: **23**

Maximum number of years a Zimbabwean can be imprisoned for ridiculing President Robert Mugabe: **5**

CIVICS

Estimated number of Chinese who have been "detained" by the government for prodemocracy activities since the Tiananmen Square massacre in 1989: **20,000**

Amount the Chinese government charged next of kin, in 1989, for each bullet used in an execution: **13¢**

Number of people shot in the back of the head by New York City police during the 1980s: **5**

Number of Americans sentenced to death since 1900 who were later found to be innocent: **139**

Number of prisoners on death row who have committed suicide, have been murdered, or have died of natural causes since 1977: **73**

Number of inmates in New York City jails who have committed suicide since 1986: **15**

Cost of building a new maximum-security prison, per cell: **$50,000**

Average prison sentence handed down in U.S. security-fraud cases since 1978, in months: **14**

Amount trader Dennis Levine earned on the maintenance crew at the Lewisburg Federal Prison while serving a two-year sentence there: **$1,200**

Years it would take Jim Bakker to earn enough to pay his federal fine on his wages cleaning prison toilets: **2,331**

Total number of days of his three-year prison sentence that Oliver North served: **0**

Number of days in prison Zsa Zsa Gabor served in 1989 for slapping a police officer: **3**

THE DRUG WAR

Chances that a federal prison inmate is serving a sentence for drug dealing: **1 in 2**

Rank of drugs among the "gravest domestic threats facing our nation," according to President Bush in 1989: **1**

Antidrug spending proposed by the Bush administration for 1991, expressed as a percentage of the federal budget: **0.86**

Percentage of the $10.6 billion 1990 federal antidrug budget that went to law enforcement: **71**

Percentage that went to educational programs: **13**

Chances that an illegal-drug user is white: **4 in 5**

Estimated expense incurred by an untreated drug addict, in health, welfare, law enforcement, and productivity costs in New York State: **$15,262**

Average cost of successfully treating a drug addict in a non-residential program in New York State: **$3,500**

Percentage of state and local district attorneys who say that marijuana should be legalized: **25**

CIVICS

Amount the Tobacco Institute donated to underwrite the antidrug booklet *Helping Youth Say No*: **$70,000**

Chances that a first-time cigarette smoker will become addicted: **9 in 10**

Chances that a first-time user of crack cocaine will become addicted: **1 in 3**

Chances that an American born in 1990 was exposed to illegal drugs *in utero*: **1 in 10**

Percentage of the marijuana smoked in the United States in 1985 that was imported: **45**

Percentage today that is: **70**

Minimum number of tons that a Miami marijuana seizure must weigh before the federal government will assist in prosecution: **2.5**

Amount by which cash deposits exceeded cash withdrawals at banks in Miami in 1989: **$5,097,011,000**

Rank of the Miami Federal Reserve, among all Reserve branches, in the size of its cash surplus in 1990: **1**

Percentage of all paper money in the United States that contains traces of cocaine: **97**

Members of the Panamanian cabinet who have owned or directed banks accused of laundering drug money: **5**

Percentage of Peru's annual coca crop destroyed by U.S.-assisted forces in 1989: **1**

Percentage destroyed by insects: **20**

Ratio of the amount of cocaine seized by the Colombian military to the amount seized by the Colombian police in 1988: **1:4**

Ratio of U.S. emergency aid received by the Colombian military to aid received by the Colombian police in 1988: **6:1**

Percentage of job applicants to the Houston Police Department who acknowledge that they have smoked marijuana: **50**

Bounty that drug smugglers are rumored to have put on Barco, a U.S. Border Patrol drug-sniffing dog: **$30,000**

Reward the Colombian army offered in 1990 for the capture of Medellín drug lord Pablo Escobar: **$400,000**

Reward Escobar offered for "the head" of Colombia's investigative police chief: **$1,000,000**

Number of deaths in Colombia since 1988 that have been attributed to retaliation for national extradition policies in narcotics cases: **951**

Ratio of Coast Guard employees disciplined for drug violations to drug smugglers caught by the Coast Guard in 1988: **1:3**

Number of the 4,798 U.S. Customs Service employees screened for drugs since 1986 who tested positive: **2**

Value of the narcotics that the U.S. Border Patrol's thirty-eight hundred agents detected in 1989, per agent: **$54,737**

Value of the narcotics that the Patrol's ninety drug-sniffing dogs detected, per dog: **$1,001,890**

Hourly rate for hiring a trained dog and handler to conduct a drug search of an office, from Interquest of Houston: **$60**

Portion of the U.S. marijuana crop that is grown indoors: **1/4**

Percentage of Americans who say they approve of searching homes without a warrant in order to combat drugs: **52**

Price of a can of DrugAlert, a spray that detects traces of illegal drugs on household surfaces: **$16.65**

Amount of dehydrated, drug-free urine sold since 1986 by Byrd Laboratories of Austin, Texas, in reconstituted gallons: **2,656**

SECRECY

Number of documents classified as "secret" or "top secret" by the U.S. government in 1989: **5,506,720**

Percentage change, since 1982, in the number of federal employees with security clearances: **−22**

Number of personal-computer disks seized by Secret Service agents in May 1990: **23,000**

Amount the British government spent in 1988 to stop publication of *Spycatcher*, a memoir by a former intelligence officer: **$6,000,000**

Amount the U.S. government spent on paper shredders in 1989: **$7,000,000**

Number of pages in Andy Warhol's 72-page FBI file that the bureau refuses to release: **33**

Number of Americans arrested for spying on the United States between 1970 and 1980: **9**

Number arrested since 1980: **40**

Amount the IRS claims convicted spy John Walker owes in back taxes on income he earned from spying: **$252,500**

Number of toll-free calls received by the U.S. Army's spy information hot line in 1989: **23,408**

Number of Americans who have received new identities under the Federal Witness Security Program: **12,600**

Average cost of having an office checked for wiretaps and debugged: **$3,500**

Percentage of Fortune 500 companies that test employees and job applicants for illegal drug use: **55**

Estimated number of Americans who have counterfeit diplomas or credentials: **500,000**

Government estimate of the value of the untaxed U.S. economy: **$84,000,000,000**

Percentage of executives who rank themselves as their "most trusted confidant in an ethical situation": **44**

Percentage of cat owners who say they confide in their cats about important matters: **57**

SOCIAL STUDIES

The Battle of the Sexes

Black and White

Childhood

Adolescence

Fads

Traditions

Giving and Receiving

Making It Big

THE BATTLE OF THE SEXES

Chances that a married American working woman earns more than her husband: **1 in 5**

Average percentage change in an American man's standard of living in the year after a divorce: **+43**

Average percentage change in a woman's standard of living: **−73**

Chances that an American woman considers herself a strong supporter of the women's movement: **1 in 5**

Chances that an American woman is married, has children, and says she has a "successful career": **2 in 5**

Percentage of American women who say they prefer a female boss: **15**

Percentage who say they prefer a male boss: **54**

Percentage of American women who said in 1970 that men were "basically kind, gentle, and thoughtful": **67**

Percentage who say this today: **51**

Chances that an American woman thinks she would do "better than average" in a fistfight: **1 in 4**

Ratio of the average number of times a woman cries each month to the average number of times a man does: **4:1**

Ratio of the number of dreams men have about men to the number they have about women: **2:1**

Average number of disclaimers an American man makes before telling a joke: **1.9**

Average number an American woman makes: **3.4**

Chances that a condom bought in the United States is purchased by a woman: **1 in 5**

Average number of articles of clothing bought by an American man each year: **35**

Average number bought by an American woman: **54**

Percentage of American men who "care how their feet look": **77**

Maximum amount of time most American men say they want to spend cooking a meal, in minutes: **15**

Maximum amount of time most American women say they want to spend cooking a meal, in minutes: **30**

Number of Betty Rubble tablets in a bottle of Flintstones Chewable Vitamins: **0**

Percentage of women who say they control the TV remote control in their household: **34**

Percentage of men who say they control the TV remote: **56**

Average walking speed of an American man, in feet per minute: **275**

SOCIAL STUDIES

Average walking speed of an American woman, in feet per minute: **274**

Percentage of men who say their biggest thrill would be to get the winning hit in the World Series: **32**

Percentage of women who say this: **37**

Chances that an American in 1975 thought that men had a better life than women: **1 in 3**

Chances that an American thinks so today: **1 in 2**

Estimated number of U.S. colleges and universities that offer courses in "men's studies": **350**

BLACK AND WHITE

Chances that a black American man will be murdered: **1 in 30**

Chances that a black American man was in state or federal prison in 1980: **1 in 50**

Chances today: **1 in 36**

Number of the 84 appeals-court judges appointed by Ronald Reagan who are white men: **73**

Percentage of American gun owners who are black: **6**

Percentage who are white: **88**

WHAT COUNTS

Change, since 1984, in the life expectancy of a white American, in years: **+0.2**

Change in the life expectancy of a black American, in years: **−0.2**

Average number of months a black American waits for a kidney transplant: **13.9**

Average number of months a white American waits: **7.6**

Number of black Americans, per 100,000, who commit suicide each year: **7**

Number of white Americans, per 100,000, who do: **14**

Rank of white, Hispanic, and black girls among those who lose the most self-esteem during puberty: **1, 2, 3**

Percentage of black high-school graduates under the age of twenty-five who were unemployed in 1989: **21**

Percentage of white high-school dropouts under the age of twenty-five who were: **18**

Chances that a black American who attends college will attend a black college: **1 in 6**

Chances that a black American who graduates from college will graduate from a black college: **1 in 3**

Percentage of American college students who say that some races are "more evolved" than others: **45**

Percentage increase since 1988 in the number of black students who belong to fraternities or sororities: **115**

SOCIAL STUDIES

Percentage of blacks who say that college athletes should be paid: **37**

Percentage of whites who say this: **16**

Number of the 250 newspaper reporters covering major-league baseball teams who are black: **2**

Number of the 10 athletes who have appeared most frequently on the cover of *Sports Illustrated* who are black: **4**

Number of the 11 magazine articles about lottery winners published in 1989 that ran in *Jet* magazine: **11**

Percentage of all billboards in black neighborhoods in Baltimore that advertise alcohol or tobacco: **76**

Percentage of all billboards in white neighborhoods in Baltimore that do: **20**

Chances that a man living in Harlem will live past the age of sixty-five: **2 in 5**

Chances that a man living in Bangladesh will: **3 in 5**

Percentage of black New Yorkers who believe it is possible that AIDS is a plot against blacks: **30**

Percentage of blacks in the New York City area who would have to move into a different neighborhood for the area's races to be evenly distributed: **80**

Chances that an American who was overlooked in the 1980 census was black, according to the Census Bureau: **1 in 2**

Percentage of black mayors who head cities that don't have a black majority: **35**

WHAT COUNTS

Average number of publications issued by the U.S. Civil Rights Commission each year from 1957 to 1983: **51**

Average number issued each year since 1983: **13**

Percentage of blacks who say that peacetime military service is "a very important obligation": **45**

Percentage of whites who say this: **31**

Percentage of Americans who believe that blacks "should not push themselves where they are not wanted": **58**

Percentage of all rapes in the United States since 1979 in which the victim and the assailant were of the same race: **79**

Percentage change in the birthrate for single black women from 1976 to 1986: **−9**

Percentage change in the birthrate for single black women since 1986: **+13**

Percentage of babies born to unmarried white women under the age of seventeen that are given up for adoption: **17**

Percentage of babies born to unmarried black women under the age of seventeen that are given up: **1**

Percentage of foreign babies adopted by Americans that come from Africa: **0.4**

Percentage of Americans who believe there should be a law against interracial marriages: **21**

Percentage change in Ku Klux Klan membership since 1980: **−50**

Percentage increase, since 1977, in the number of marriages between blacks and whites in the United States: **59**

Number of blacks among the 5 Americans admired most by teenagers: **3**

CHILDHOOD

Average number of U.S. presidents an eight- to twelve-year-old American child can name: **4.8**

Average number of alcoholic beverages an eight- to twelve-year-old American child can name: **5.2**

Average number of minutes per weekday that the child of a working mother watches television: **111**

Average number of minutes per weekday that the child of a nonworking mother watches television: **139**

Estimated average number of murders an American child has seen on television by age sixteen: **10,000**

Portion of all deaths worldwide that are of children under the age of five in developing countries: **1/3**

Estimated number of soldiers worldwide who are under the age of fifteen: **100,000**

Estimated percentage of Palestinian stone-throwers in the Occupied Territories who are under the age of thirteen: **60**

Price of a child-size bulletproof denim jacket from the Guardian Group in New York City: **$500**

Chances that the death of a ten- to fourteen-year-old American in 1968 was a suicide: **1 in 69**

Chances today: **1 in 17**

Percentage increase, since 1950, in the incidence of cancer among American children: **22**

Percentage increase, since 1977, in the number of American children diagnosed as having learning disabilities: **142**

Average number of words in the written vocabulary of a six- to fourteen-year-old American child in 1945: **25,000**

Average number today: **10,000**

Chances that a New York City child lives below the poverty line: **1 in 3**

Price of a ninety-minute children's birthday party for thirty guests at Jeremy's Place in New York City: **$650**

Average annual income of an American child: **$229.84**

Percentage of children who said in 1988 that Michael Dukakis was "highly qualified" to be president: **8**

Percentage who said that Pee-Wee Herman was: **8**

Portion of all playground injuries that occur on the monkey bars: **1/4**

Number of children crushed to death by automatic garage doors since 1982: **44**

SOCIAL STUDIES

Estimated number of referees at children's sporting events who are attacked each year by parents: **100**

Percentage of parents who say they want the option of having their child's school photograph retouched: **30**

Percentage of nine- to eleven-year-old American girls who regularly use deodorant: **58**

Percentage of American fifth graders who say they are in love: **39**

ADOLESCENCE

Percentage of American high-school students who say they want to be president of the United States: **21**

Percentage who say they want to be president of a company: **75**

Tuition for a weekend session at the Dollars ¢ Sense Management Workshop for thirteen- to fifteen-year-olds: **$500**

Chances that an American between the ages of six and seventeen cannot pass a basic fitness test: **2 in 3**

Percentage of teenage boys who say they worry about losing their hair: **29**

Percentage of teenage girls who say they do: **36**

Change, between the ages of nine and fourteen, in the percentage of American girls who say "I am happy the way I am": −31

Change in the percentage of boys who say this: −21

Percentage of male high-school seniors who say they have used steroids: 7

Chances that a homosexual teenage boy will attempt suicide: 1 in 3

Chances that an unwed teenage mother will become pregnant again within a year of giving birth: 1 in 5

Chances that a teenage girl living in the South Bronx was pregnant in 1989: 1 in 6

Chances that a first-time bride in Kentucky is a teenager: 1 in 3

Number of American boys under the age of fifteen who were arrested for forcible rape in 1989: 1,574

Percentage of sixth- to twelfth-grade boys who say it is acceptable for a man to rape his date if he has spent "a lot of money" on her: 22

Percentage of ninth-grade boys who say they have "hit or beat up another kid" in the past year: 64

Ratio of teenage victims of homicide to teenage suicides in the United States: 1:1

Percentage of Americans who say that "lack of opportunity due to poverty" is a main cause of teenage violence: 50

Percentage who say that "rock lyrics that glorify sex and violence" are a main cause of teenage violence: **52**

Percentage of teenagers who say the world is "getting worse": **45**

Percentage of American high-school students who cannot name the region of the country William Faulkner wrote about: **67**

Percentage of high-school students who say the telephone was invented after 1950: **10**

Amount a Florida mother sought in a 1989 lawsuit against a teenager who stood her daughter up for a prom date: **$49.53**

Percentage of American teenagers who say they want to be like their parents: **39**

Percentage of American teenagers who say they believe in the existence of angels: **74**

FADS

Tons of the Berlin Wall shipped to the United States since November 1989 by Hyman Products of St. Louis: **59**

Number of days after the U.S. invasion of Panama that an Oregon software company introduced a computer game called Find Noriega!: **2**

Number of times Manuel Noriega's prison number was bet in the first Florida state lottery held after he was arrested: **12,139**

Number of books published in the 1980s with the word *Terrorism* in the title: **190**

Price of a flame-retardant American flag from the Freedom Writer group of Great Barrington, Massachusetts: **$10**

Brands of bottled water sold in the United States: **575**

Percentage increase in U.S. sales of Mexican beer since 1984: **245**

Percentage of Americans who said in 1985 that they had never heard the word *yuppie*: **39**

Number of indoor miniature-golf courses built in the United States in 1990: **17**

Percentage of Jeeps sold in the United States in 1990 that were bought by people living in urban or suburban areas: **67**

Percentage of Iowans who own lawn ornaments: **24**

Estimated number of plastic pink flamingos sold in the United States in 1990: **500,000**

Percentage increase, during the 1980s, in the use of the term *postmodern* by *The New York Times*: **237**

Lines of coke done in the book *Bright Lights, Big City*: **48**

Number of people in the world who speak Esperanto: **1,000,000**

Number of adults in the San Francisco area who have completed est training: **500,000**

Percentage of Pepsi drinkers who say they would switch to Coke if it contained oat bran: **74**

TRADITIONS

Percentage of Iowans who say that front-porch swings "should be brought back": **57**

Percentage of male farmers in Iowa who own a pair of bib overalls: **41**

Estimated number of one-room schoolhouses in Nebraska: **300**

Number of recipes that call for a can of cream soup in *Aggies, Moms, and Apple Pie*, a cookbook published by Texas A&M University: **41**

Rank of steak and potatoes, among Americans' favorite meals: **1**

Rank of gin and tonics and martinis, among the most popular drinks in American bars and restaurants: **1, 2**

Cups of tea the average Briton drinks each day: **3.7**

Gallons of mint juleps drunk each year at the Kentucky Derby: **2,000**

WHAT COUNTS

Number of wild horses in the American West: **44,000**

Number of people who have barreled over Niagara Falls and survived: **9**

Amount that the city of La Mancha, Spain, has spent to restore its medieval and Renaissance windmills: **$78,500**

Number of Americans who have a lifetime subscription to *Reader's Digest*: **38,961**

Number of *National Geographic* subscribers who have canceled their subscriptions to protest its use of metric measurements: **155**

Number of inquiries about John Dillinger's penis received by the Smithsonian Institution each year: **10**

Percentage of teenagers who lost their virginity in a car: **12**

GIVING AND RECEIVING

Percentage of Americans who say they didn't like what they got for Christmas last year: **6**

Estimated average value of the toys that an American child receives as gifts each year: **$300**

Amount Americans spent in 1989 on toy guns: **$108,800,000**

Estimated number of Ant Farms sold each hour: **46**

Number of prizes given away in boxes of Cracker Jack since 1912: **16,000,000,000**

Number of condoms that New York City distributed to community organizations in 1989: **3,300,000**

Estimated number of Thai men who receive free vasectomies each year on the king's birthday: **1,000**

Pairs of socks received as gifts by George Bush when he was vice-president: **48**

Percentage of the ties sold each year that are bought for Father's Day: **17**

Floral arrangements delivered to Graceland each year on the anniversary of Elvis Presley's death: **60**

Percentage of Americans who say they are "very likely" to become organ donors: **20**

Percentage of Americans who say they are "very likely" to donate a "loved one's organs": **78**

MAKING IT BIG

Amount that Robin Weir, Nancy Reagan's former hairdresser, charges for a haircut: **$150**

Amount that he charges for a speech: **$1,000**

Increase in Maki Mandela's lecture fee since her father was released from prison: **$1,000**

Rank of photographs of President Nixon with Elvis Presley, among those most often requested from the National Archives: **1**

Number of galleries that have exhibited paintings and prints by Tony Bennett: **58**

Number of universities that have a Barbra Streisand Professor of Women and Men in Society: **1**

Amount given to Florida State University to endow the Burt Reynolds Eminent Scholar chair in theater: **$600,000**

Number of years Charles Nelson Reilly has held the chair: **2**

Number of honorary degrees Frank Sinatra has been awarded: **3**

Number that Bob Hope has been awarded: **53**

Number of filing cabinets full of jokes in Hope's fireproof vaults: **34**

Number of these that contain jokes he has not yet used: **16**

Average number of jokes in a forty-minute Henny Youngman monologue: **245**

Number of times Bill Cosby's name appears in the closing credits for "The Cosby Show": **4**

Total number of guests Joe Franklin has had on his TV show: **187,215**

SOCIAL STUDIES

Percentage of French men who say they would like to see Princess Stephanie pose nude in a magazine: **28**

Rank of Madonna, Elizabeth Taylor, Donald Trump, and Saddam Hussein, in number of magazine-cover appearances in 1990: **1, 2, 3, 4**

Percentage of American men who say they would not have sex with Madonna if she asked: **60**

HISTORY

■▪■▪■▪■▪■▪■▪■▪■▪■▪■▪■▪■▪■▪■▪■▪■

THE REAGAN YEARS

Total number of times Ronald Reagan publicly mentioned the savings-and-loan crisis during his presidency: **0**

Federal spending on the military during the Reagan administration, per second: **$8,730**

Chances that a dollar of U.S. foreign aid in 1980 was military aid: **1 in 4**

Chances in 1988: **2 in 5**

Percentage increase in the number of job applications received by the CIA between 1984 and 1989: **50**

Change, since 1980, in the percentage of their income the poorest 20 percent of American families pay in federal taxes: **+16**

Change in the percentage of their income the richest 1 percent of American families pay: **−14**

Ratio of the average number of times each year that Ronald Reagan awarded a Medal of Freedom to the number of times that Jimmy Carter did: **2:1**

Average number of feet that separated Jimmy Carter from reporters each time he walked from the White House to his helicopter: **2**

Average number of feet that separated Ronald Reagan from reporters: **50**

Ratio of the number of presidential press conferences held during Reagan's first year in office to those held in Bush's first year: **1:5**

Number of speeches Ronald Reagan made on the subject of AIDS during his presidency: **2**

Ratio of the U.S. government's budget for housing to its budget for the military in 1980: **1:5**

Ratio in 1990: **1:34**

Amount the federal government paid outside consultants in 1988: **$4,900,000,000**

Percentage change, between 1982 and 1989, in the number of federal employees: **+30**

Percentage of Americans who said in 1987 that "many problems are beyond the president's grasp": **50**

Percentage who said that President Reagan "always tells the truth": **8**

Number of times Edwin Meese used some form of the statement "I don't recall" during his two days of Iran-Contra testimony in 1989: **340**

Estimated total amount the U.S. government paid Manuel Noriega during the Reagan administration: **$1,200,000**

Amount the U.S. government paid Romania between 1979 and 1989 for Soviet-made weapons for intelligence purposes: **$40,000,000**

Estimated amount of the payment that went directly into the Ceauşescu family's private bank accounts: **$8,000,000**

Number of months it took Ronald Reagan to read Mikhail Gorbachev's book *Perestroika*: **6**

Number of times that Ronald Reagan has been quoted as saying "Doveryai no proveryai" (trust but verify) in *The New York Times*: **11**

Percentage of eighteen- to twenty-four-year-olds who said in 1988 that they preferred President Reagan's hairstyle to Carter's and Ford's: **47**

Tons of jelly beans the White House purchased from the Herman Goelitz Candy Company during the Reagan presidency: **12**

Number of lines in Ronald Reagan's entry in the 1990 edition of *Who's Who in America*: **10**

Number of lines in Nancy Reagan's entry: **28**

Federal funds spent to move the Reagans out of the White House: **$1,250,000**

THE GORBACHEV LEGACY

Average number of times Mikhail Gorbachev has been mentioned in *The New York Times* since becoming Soviet president in 1985, per month: **161**

Number of months Nikita Khrushchev's son Sergei spent as a fellow at Harvard's Institute of Politics in 1990: **3**

Number of designs submitted by Soviets in 1988 for a national memorial to those who died under Stalin: **176**

Price of a videotape of Andrei Sakharov's funeral, from Tass: **$1,500**

Number of months after being released from prison that Václav Havel was elected president of Czechoslovakia: **7**

Total number of years served in prison by the members of the Polish parliament elected in 1989: **117**

Portion of the buildings under construction in Poland in 1990 that were Catholic churches: **1/3**

Estimated value of Polish zlotys held in Polish bank accounts in 1989: **$600,000,000**

Estimated value of foreign currency held in Polish bank accounts in 1989: **$3,918,000,000**

Amount the German government has pledged to pay the Soviet Union to resettle troops stationed in what was formerly East Germany: **$2,700,000,000**

Change in the value of stock of the top ten U.S. defense contractors in the month after the opening of the Berlin Wall: **−$1,140,000,000**

Price of the Russian-language version of Monopoly, from Parker Brothers: **$39**

Price of a "perestroika" button from a Moscow street vendor in January 1988: **$1.60**

Percentage of Muscovites who said in 1989 that "average people don't have any say about what the government does": **43**

Percentage of New Yorkers who said this: **52**

Ratio of the average rental price of office space in Moscow's business district in 1990 to the average price in midtown Manhattan, per square foot: **2:1**

Number of new businesses that were started in Poland in 1990: **175,000**

Number of businesses that folded in Poland in 1990: **147,000**

Number of former West Germans expected to file claims for property that became part of East Germany after 1949: **500,000**

Number of neo-Nazi criminal indictments in East Germany in 1988: **44**

Number in 1989: **144**

Percentage increase, since 1989, in the number of riot-control troops in the Soviet Union: **250**

Percentage increase, since 1988, in the number of thefts of firearms, ammunition, and explosives in the Soviet Union: **100**

Number of the 15 republics in the Soviet Union in which there are independence movements: **15**

Number of the 21 members of the Politburo and Secretariat who have resigned or been fired since Gorbachev came to power: **16**

Number of Soviet Army officers in Siberia who are assigned full-time to locating deserters: **100**

Amount of food the Indian government pledged in 1990 to donate to the Soviet Union, in tons: **20,000**

Average percentage of a Polish family's income that is spent on food: **70**

Chances that a Pole's favorite TV show is "Dynasty": **1 in 4**

Price of a "saddle of love" from Intersex, a newly opened sexual-novelty shop in Warsaw, in zlotys: **724,000**

Price of registering with Moscow's American-Russian Match-making service, in rubles: **50**

Payment David Letterman made to Miss USSR for appearing on his show in 1990, in cartons of Marlboros: **4**

MILITARY AFFAIRS

Average daily cost of the Civil War, in 1990 dollars: **$33,000,000**

Average daily cost of the Vietnam War, in 1990 dollars: **$72,000,000**

Average daily cost of the Persian Gulf War: **$1,000,000,000**

Percentage change, since 1981, in the amount the Pentagon spends each year on classified projects: **+272**

Percentage of all U.S. defense contracts awarded in 1990 through thoroughly competitive bidding: **11**

Fine General Dynamics paid the Pentagon in 1985 for "improper activities," expressed as a percentage of the company's 1985 contracts: **0.00009**

Number of ethics directors employed by General Dynamics in 1990: **32**

Percentage of the $9,900,000 cost of converting the Veterans Administration to a Cabinet department that was spent on signs: **86**

Medals awarded by the U.S. military for the 1983 action in Grenada: **12,933**

Number of condoms the U.S. Defense Personnel Support Center purchased for the armed services in 1989: **7,632,000**

Pairs of green socks the center purchased: **5,118,470**

Number of sizes of women's dress uniform offered by the U.S. Army in 1990: **48**

Number offered in 1989: **105**

Amount the U.S. Air Force spends each year on imported-goatskin flight jackets: **$3,800,000**

Number of months after the Pentagon bought eighty thousand camouflage helmet-covers in 1989 that it found another eighty thousand in storage: **3**

Average amount of paper and filing cabinets carried on a U.S. Navy guided-missile frigate, in tons: **14**

Average amount of toilet paper used each day in the Pentagon, in rolls: **666**

Amount the Pentagon spent on each spare toilet-seat cover for its C-5B cargo plane in 1989: **$1,868.15**

Amount the Pentagon spent in 1989 on test samples of marijuana-laced, freeze-dried urine: **$18,110**

Amount the U.S. Air Force spent in 1990 to study the effects of jet noise on pregnant horses: **$100,000**

Amount the Pentagon "saved" by moving the first payday of fiscal 1990 back to fiscal 1989: **$3,000,000,000**

Amount the U.S. Air Force has spent since 1981 on matchbooks and playing cards for Air Force One and Two: **$150,000**

Pounds of Saudi Arabian sand the U.S. Army imported in 1990 to research its effect on military equipment: **150**

Number of empty sandbags the U.S. Army shipped to Saudi Arabia in August 1990: **2,000,000**

Bottles of suntan lotion the U.S. Army purchased from a K mart in Hinesville, Georgia, in the month after Iraq invaded Kuwait: **25,550**

MILITARY PERSONNEL

Ratio of the average amount the United States spends fighting a war to the average amount it spends on each war's veterans' benefits: **1:3**

Portion of the U.S. population that is eligible for some form of veterans' benefits: **1/3**

Number of Americans who received veterans' benefits in 1990 for a relative's service in the Civil War: **51**

Total amount of veterans' benefits mistakenly paid in 1989 directly to veterans who were no longer alive: **$5,700,000**

Medals awarded by the U.S. armed forces in 1989, per day: **1,148**

Ratio of GI Joe dolls to American GIs: **50:1**

Ratio of admirals to ships in the U.S. Navy in 1945: **1:130**

WHAT COUNTS

Ratio today: **1:2**

Number of historians employed by the Pentagon: **397**

Number of courses on the Vietnam War required for graduation from West Point: **0**

Number of U.S. Air Force personnel assigned to criminal investigation and counterintelligence: **1,548**

Number assigned to public affairs: **1,417**

Percentage of Pentagon officers who retired between 1985 and 1987 who now work for defense contractors: **15**

Number of candidates who declined the job of undersecretary for acquisition at the Pentagon in 1990: **47**

Percentage of the U.S. Marines discharged in 1988 for homosexuality who were women: **32**

Percentage of U.S. Marines in 1988 who were women: **5**

Amount the military spent recruiting and training the 1,075 homosexuals it discharged in 1988: **$13,221,425**

Number of dolphins, sea lions, and whales being trained in "surveillance and detection" by the U.S. Navy: **139**

Number of cats the U.S. Army has shot in the head since 1983 to research battlefield injuries: **648**

Estimated number of mules the Reagan administration shipped to Afghan rebels during the 1980s: **1,178**

Estimated number of cockroaches in the Pentagon: **2,000,000**

WEAPONRY

Number of states in which some part of the B-2 bomber has been developed or manufactured: **50**

Number of states in which nuclear weapons are deployed: **25**

Percentage of Americans who believe that the United States has never used nuclear weapons in war: **11**

Federal spending in 1990 on construction of U.S. nuclear-weapons plants: **$589,000,000**

Federal spending in 1990 on cleanups of U.S. nuclear-weapons plants: **$2,750,000,000**

Change, since 1988, in federal funds spent on chemical-weapons production: **−$124,500,000**

Change, since 1988, in federal funds spent on chemical-weapons destruction: **+$205,200,000**

Estimated number of countries that have the ability to produce chemical weapons: **20**

Estimated amount of time it takes to dismantle one U.S. Army tank, in man-hours: **120**

Value of the arms that Warsaw Pact members bought from NATO countries between 1980 and 1988: **$200,000,000**

Value of the arms that NATO members bought from Warsaw Pact countries: **$100,000,000**

Ratio of Soviet arms sales to Third World countries to U.S. arms sales to Third World countries in 1986: **4:1**

Ratio in 1989: **1:1**

Estimated number of unexploded land and trip mines left in Afghanistan after the withdrawal of Soviet troops in 1989: **20,000,000**

Ratio of unexploded land mines to people on the Falkland Islands: **7:1**

Number of crossbows in Britain: **280,000**

Number of privately registered machine guns in the United States: **194,966**

Chances that an American gun owner's gun is loaded: **1 in 3**

Price of a gold-plated .44 Magnum pistol issued in 1989 to commemorate the Second Amendment to the Constitution: **$1,895**

Value of a B-2 bomber's weight in gold, expressed as a percentage of an actual bomber's cost: **57**

Pounds of butter that can be bought for the cost of an M-16 rifle: **288**

CASUALTIES OF WAR

Estimated number of deaths in armed conflicts worldwide during the 1980s: **5,600,000**

Percentage of the casualties in all armed conflicts since 1980 who were civilians: **75**

Deaths caused by terrorism, worldwide, in 1979: **165**

In 1989: **325**

Percentage of all those killed or injured in terrorist bombings worldwide in 1989 who were Pakistani: **30**

Estimated number of POWs from the Iran-Iraq War who were still imprisoned two years after the cease-fire: **100,000**

Number of days after a truck bomb killed 241 U.S. Marines in Beirut that the United States invaded Grenada: **2**

Ratio of U.S. soldiers killed to those wounded in the U.S. invasion of Panama: **1:14**

Ratio of Panamanian soldiers killed to those wounded: **2:1**

Ratio of per capita Nicaraguan deaths in their civil war to per capita American deaths in the Vietnam War: **33:1**

Number of walls the size of the Vietnam Memorial it would

take to list the names of all the Vietnamese who died in the war: **69**

Chances that a Vietnam veteran has suffered from post-traumatic stress disorder: **1 in 3**

Number of Americans declared missing in action during the Vietnam War: **2,300**

Number of Americans declared missing in action during World War II: **78,751**

Estimated percentage of the Soviet Union's population that was killed in World War II: **13**

Percentage of Afghanistan's population that has been killed since the Soviet invasion in 1980: **7**

Percentage of Angola's population that has never lived during peacetime: **71**

Number of armed conflicts in Africa in 1990: **11**

Portion of the 115 armed conflicts worldwide in 1990 that were civil wars: **9/10**

Percentage of armed conflicts in the twentieth century that were won by the country or faction that started them: **39**

Percentage of conflicts during the 1980s that were: **15**

DÉJÀ VU

Members of the 70's Preservation Society: **36,000**

Price paid in 1987 in West Virginia for a case of Billy Beer: **$2,000**

Number of years Steve Jenne of Springfield, Illinois, has saved a buffalo sandwich bitten into by Richard Nixon: **30**

Average number of people who listen to the Watergate tapes at the National Archives each week: **12**

Percentage increase, since 1984, in the number of job inquiries to the Peace Corps: **176**

Number of police officers needed to evict the last resident of the Memphis motel where a Martin Luther King museum is planned: **4**

Number of times Abbie Hoffman was arrested in his lifetime: **43**

Number of the 23 cast members of the 1989 Chicago production of *Hair* who wore wigs: **20**

Number of Americans who live on communes: **40,000**

Estimated number of time capsules buried worldwide: **10,000**

Number of times Mick Jagger has appeared on the cover of *Rolling Stone*: **15**

WHAT COUNTS

Hours that "Father Knows Best" is on the air each week in Des Moines: **5**

New episodes of "Perry Mason" produced since 1985: **16**

Total time that the song "Yesterday" has been broadcast or performed since it was written in 1965, in years: **31**

Estimated number of seconds that humans perceive "the present" to last: **3**

Chances that a deep breath inhaled today will contain a molecule from Julius Caesar's dying breath: **99 in 100**

Percentage of Americans who say they have never experienced déjà vu: **42**

GEOGRAPHY

State of the World
Latin America
The Middle East
Japan
Migration
Transportation
New York, New York
Southern Hospitality
American Pie

STATE OF THE WORLD

Chances that a nation's constitution was written after 1965: **3 in 4**

Number of national independence days that are in July: **12**

Number of colonies in the world: **57**

Portion of the world's population that lives under governments controlled by the military: **1/12**

Estimated number of countries in which revenue from foreign aid accounts for more than a quarter of the national budget: **40**

Portion of the world's nations that have practiced torture since 1980: **1/3**

Percentage increase, since 1969, in the number of international terrorist organizations: **469**

Percentage increase, since 1980, in the amount spent on UN peace missions: **133**

Total number of vetoes cast by the Soviet Union in the UN Security Council during the 1980s: **4**

WHAT COUNTS

Total number cast by the United States: **48**

Number of countries that have been invaded since 1945: **23**

Number of these invasions the United States has sent troops to help repel: **3**

Percentage of Canadians who said in 1988 that they would prefer communism to nuclear war: **60**

Percentage of Americans in 1988 who believed that the Soviet Union was a member of NATO: **16**

Number of people in the United States who are studying Russian: **57,000**

Number of people in the Soviet Union who are studying English: **4,200,000**

Estimated portion of the world's six thousand languages that have no speakers under the age of twelve: **1/3**

Percentage of Chinese teenagers who can correctly identify the size of the world's population: **85**

Percentage of American adults who can: **35**

Number of countries with zero population growth in 1990: **2**

Number of participants in the All-India Conference of Eunuchs, held in Ghonsla in 1990: **1,000**

Number of condoms the U.S. government has distributed to developing countries since 1981: **5,365,000,000**

Percentage of the world's legislators who are women: **12**

GEOGRAPHY

Percentage of the members of the Supreme Soviet in 1990 who were in office in 1984: **10**

Percentage of the members of the U.S. Senate in 1990 who were in office in 1984: **70**

Number of revolutions that Polish journalist Ryszard Kapuściński has witnessed in the 36 years he has been reporting: **27**

Percentage change, since 1985, in U.S. funding for overseas refugees: **−30**

Percentage change, since 1985, in the number of refugees worldwide: **+50**

Estimated change in the distance between the Hawaiian Islands and the Soviet Union each year, in inches: **−4**

Number of people meditating simultaneously needed to affect world affairs, according to the Maharishi Mahesh Yogi: **7,000**

LATIN AMERICA

Average number of Latin American countries the United States has invaded and occupied each decade since 1900: **5**

Ratio of Latin America's total foreign debt to the amount of U.S. aid President Bush pledged to the region for 1991: **400:1**

Amount the U.S. government lent Brazil in 1989 to build a highway through the Amazon rain forest: **$20,000,000**

Portion of the land in Nicaragua that was owned by the government under the Sandinista regime: **1/9**

Portion of the land in the United States that is owned by the government: **1/3**

Number of congressional votes dealing with Nicaragua that have taken place since 1980: **90**

Percentage of Americans in 1986 who knew which side the United States supported in Nicaragua: **50**

Number of the 173 private religious schools in Nicaragua under the Sandinista regime that were subsidized by the government: **121**

Number of babies baptized in Cuba in 1988: **45,000**

Number of Soviet and Cuban military ground personnel in Central America: **0**

Number of U.S. military ground personnel in Central America: **13,283**

Chances that a CIA officer stationed in Mexico City can speak Spanish: **1 in 5**

Tons of weapons Fidel Castro brought with him to Brazil's presidential inauguration ceremonies in 1990: **10**

Percentage of the Brazilians who voted in the 1989 presidential election who had never voted before: **70**

Total amount of U.S. network TV airtime devoted to the national elections in Chile and Brazil in 1989, in minutes: **2**

Amount Peru's president-elect, Alberto Fujimori, spent on his campaign, per vote: **2¢**

Amount the Nicaraguan government spent to hold the country's 1990 national election, per voter: **$14**

Average monthly salary of a Nicaraguan at the time of the election: **$25**

Unemployment rate in Grenada in 1982, the year before the U.S. invasion: **14%**

Unemployment rate in Grenada today: **26%**

Chances that a Brazilian suffers from malnutrition: **2 in 3**

Percentage of the ninety thousand Latin Americans who have been "disappeared" since 1963 who were Guatemalan: **40**

Number of officially recognized death squads operating in Colombia: **140**

Number of El Salvador's 15 highest-ranking officers whose troops have committed "brutal human-rights abuses," according to the United States: **14**

Number of these officers who received U.S. training: **12**

Percentage of Salvadoran government revenues in 1988 that consisted of U.S. aid: **51**

Percentage of Americans who don't know which side the U.S. government supports in El Salvador: **40**

Percentage of Americans who do not know which country will control the Panama Canal in the year 2000: **64**

Percentage who say they followed the U.S. invasion of Panama "very closely": **60**

Average number of Panamanians detained each day in the month after the U.S. invasion for "impeding the renewal of the power of the state": **300**

Number of mayors in El Salvador who have resigned or been killed since 1988: **96**

Deaths in Colombia, since 1988, resulting from right-wing violence against opposition party representatives: **9,551**

Maximum penalty levied on Colombian government employees convicted of human-rights violations in 1990, in weeks of suspension from duty: **3**

Number of the 50 Colombian government employees convicted of human-rights violations in 1990 who received this penalty: **5**

Bail set for a Chilean soldier accused of burning a demonstrator in Santiago in July 1986: **$23**

Chances that a Latin American country has been cited for human-rights abuses since 1988: **1 in 4**

Chances that a Latin American country became a democracy during the 1980s: **2 in 5**

Price per person of a ten-day "Baseball for Peace" tour to Nicaragua, organized by Jay Feldman of Winters, California: **$1,275**

Amount of U.S. humanitarian aid the Contras spent on baseball and volleyball equipment in 1985 and 1986: **$1,245**

Amount spent on deodorant: **$5,760**

THE MIDDLE EAST

Portion of all international arms sales since 1982 that went to the Middle East: **2/5**

Percentage of U.S. foreign economic aid in 1989 that went to Israel and Egypt: **59**

Rank of Israel, the United States, and Brunei, among countries with the highest annual military expenditures per capita: **1, 2, 3**

Amount of oil used by the Pentagon in 1990, expressed as a percentage of total U.S. oil imports from Saudi Arabia: **43**

Portion of total Arab League GNP generated by countries that export oil: **2/3**

Portion of the world's Arab population that lives in an Arab League country that exports oil: **1/3**

Percentage of all children under the age of four living in Israel and the Occupied Territories who are Arab: **50**

Estimated number of stone-throwing incidents in the Occupied Territories each day: **64**

Number of the 89 people killed by tear gas during the first three years of the Palestinian uprising who were infants: **34**

Minimum amount each immigrant Soviet family receives in Israeli government subsidies: **$11,000**

Estimated percentage of Soviet immigrants to Israel in 1990 who were professionals: **55**

Percentage of land in the West Bank that is owned by Israelis: **40**

Number of mosques in the Gaza Strip: **172**

Number in 1967: **71**

Number of countries in which more than half of the population is Muslim: **36**

Percentage of the 1989 population of Kuwait who were Kuwaiti: **40**

Chances that a resident of Kuwait in 1989 was a domestic servant: **1 in 4**

Chances that an Iraqi male between the ages of fifteen and thirty-nine in 1990 was a soldier: **1 in 3**

Number of countries that sold arms to both sides during the Iran-Iraq War: **28**

Percentage of Americans who did not know in 1990 that the United States supplied arms to Iraq during its war with Iran: **73**

Percentage of the food consumed in Lebanon in 1989 that was imported: **94**

Percentage of Iowa farmers who say they support an independent Palestinian state: **40**

Percentage of "Nightline" programs about terrorism since 1985 that dealt with the Middle East: **90**

Percentage of all international acts of terrorism since 1985 that took place in the Middle East: **42**

Chances that a Palestinian male in the Occupied Territories has been arrested at least once since 1980: **1 in 10**

Number of months Israeli law permits authorities to detain a West Bank Palestinian without formal charges or trial: **12**

Percentage of Americans who said in 1988 that the United States should not send troops if an Arab country overruns Israel: **50**

Number of books about Lawrence of Arabia in print in the United States: **25**

Estimated number of princes in Saudi Arabia: **6,500**

Amount a cousin of Saudi Arabia's King Fahd lost at casinos on the French Riviera in August 1990: **$21,640,091**

Price of a gold-plated Prayer Watch indicating the direction of Mecca and five daily Muslim prayer times, from ASR of Cupertino, California: **$139**

Number of hands Saeed Al-Sayyaf, a Saudi Arabian executioner, has chopped off since he was hired in 1954: **60**

Number of heads: **600**

JAPAN

Rank of Japan, among all countries, in annual spending on nonmilitary foreign aid: **1**

Amount of money the Japanese spent in 1989 on defense: **$30,090,000,000**

Amount of money the Japanese spent in 1989 on pinball: **$99,600,000,000**

Amount of capital that Japan invested abroad in 1989, per minute: **$77,435**

Number of times Japanese banks raised the prime interest rate in 1990: **6**

Number of the 15 largest banks in California that are owned by the Japanese: **5**

Ratio of the value of U.S. real estate owned by Japanese companies to the value of U.S. real estate owned by Canadian companies: **3:5**

Number of recreational mazes in Japan: **14**

Average number of times a beer bottle in Japan is reused: **20**

Estimated number of 7-Elevens per thousand square miles in Japan: **27**

In the United States: **2**

Number of malls that opened in Japan in 1990, per month: **6**

Size of one traffic jam in Tokyo in 1990, in miles: **84**

Combined long-term corporate debt of Honda, Nissan, and Toyota: **$12,600,000,000**

Combined long-term corporate debt of Chrysler, Ford, and General Motors: **$9,000,000,000**

Average ratio of a CEO's salary to that of a blue-collar worker at major U.S. automobile manufacturers: **192:1**

Average ratio at major Japanese automobile manufacturers: **20:1**

Average portion of his or her paid vacation time that a Japanese worker takes: **1/2**

Portion of Japanese federal revenues supplied annually by corporate income taxes: **1/3**

Portion of U.S. federal revenues supplied annually by corporate income taxes: **1/10**

Estimated number of workers in the United States who are employed by Japanese companies: **212,000**

Number of manufacturing plants in Tennessee owned by Japanese companies: **90**

Number of American state governments that maintain offices in Tokyo: **39**

Number of the 206 endowed professorships at MIT that have been funded by Japanese companies: **21**

Total number of hours each school day that the children of the president of Mexico spend learning Japanese: **3**

Estimated number of haiku written by former Japanese prime minister Sousuke Uno by the time he took office in 1989: **2,000**

Winning volume in the Japanese Annual Loud Voice Contest, held in Tokyo in 1990, in decibels: **115.8**

Chances that a Japanese woman won't use a toilet outside her home: **1 in 3**

Price of a gold-plated refrigerator from the Mitsukoshi department store in Tokyo: **$6,181**

Price of a twenty-ounce box of Cheerios in Japan: **$7.30**

MIGRATION

Chances that an American lives within fifty miles of the place where he or she grew up: **1 in 2**

Average number of native-born Americans who emigrate each year: **27,000**

Number of individuals currently barred from entering the United States for political reasons: **350,000**

Percentage of legal immigrants to the United States since 1930 who were women or children: **69**

Chances that a legal immigrant to the United States comes from Asia: **1 in 2**

Percentage of legal immigrants to the United States who settle in California: **28**

Number of foreigners apprehended for illegally crossing the U.S. border in 1989: **954,119**

Average number of attempts a Mexican makes before successfully crossing the border and landing a steady job in the United States: **3**

Portion of all legal immigrants to the United States who eventually return to their country of birth: **1/3**

Number of Nicaraguans who returned to their country after the election in February 1990: **120,000**

Number of applications for political asylum submitted to the Immigration and Naturalization Service in 1979: **1,000**

Number in 1990: **101,000**

Percentage of requests by Salvadorans for political asylum in the United States in 1989 that were granted: **1**

Percentage of requests by Nicaraguans that were granted: **10**

Percentage of requests by Poles that were granted: **16**

Number of Soviet Jews who settled in Israel each week in 1990: **4,416**

Number of South Africans who emigrated each week in 1989: **112**

Number who emigrated each week in 1985: **280**

Portion of the world's refugees who are Afghans: **1/3**

Number of refugees worldwide: **15,000,000**

TRANSPORTATION

Total distance driven each year worldwide, expressed in light-years: **0.5**

Average number of months in the course of a lifetime that an American spends waiting for red lights to change: **6**

Projected average speed of cars on California's highways in the year 2010, in miles per hour: **11**

Number of convicted drunk drivers in Orange County, California, since 1988, whose sentence included a tour of the morgue: **569**

Number of them who became repeat offenders: **1**

Number of U.S. states in which it is legal to drink while driving: **9**

Amount American Airlines saved in 1987 by eliminating one olive from each salad served in first class: **$40,000**

Percentage change, between 1974 and 1989, in the amount of commercial air traffic in the United States: **+100**

Percentage change, between 1974 and 1989, in the number of commercial airports built in the United States: **0**

Percentage of U.S. passenger-airline business that was controlled by the top eight companies in 1978, the year the industry was deregulated: **81**

Percentage controlled by the top eight companies today: **93**

Percentage change, since 1978, in the number of computer, radar, and systems-maintenance technicians employed by the FAA: **−45**

Number of years it takes the average American car to produce its own weight in carbon: **1**

Percentage of motor vehicles in California that have vanity plates: **6**

Percentage in Rhode Island that do: **8**

Estimated number of U.S. billboards that are in violation of the 1965 Highway Beautification Act: **172,000**

Members of Loners on Wheels, a recreational-vehicle singles club: **2,500**

Rank of Betsy, Betty, or Bessie, among the names Iowans most often give their cars: **1**

Number of babies to whom Volkswagen has given savings bonds for being born in one of its cars: **550**

Portion of all cars that will have a microwave oven in the year 2000, according to the Campbell Soup Company: **1/4**

Percentage of Americans who keep maps in their glove compartments: **50**

Percentage who keep sunglasses in their glove compartments: **23**

Percentage who keep gloves in their glove compartments: **0**

Rank of the 1986 Chevrolet Camaro, among the cars most often stolen in the United States in 1990: **1**

Number of incidents of international terrorism since 1977 that have involved a Chevrolet Camaro: **1**

Number that have involved a BMW: **33**

Rank of Hong Kong, among localities with the most Rolls-Royces per capita: **1**

Number of rickshaws the city of Djakarta, Indonesia, has dumped into the ocean since 1985 in order to reduce traffic congestion: **100,000**

Percentage increase, since 1975, in the number of Americans who commute to work by bicycle: **5**

Ratio of the number of American suburbanites who regularly commute to another suburb to the number who commute to a city: **2:1**

Percentage of Southern California drivers who say they have made "indecent gestures" at other drivers: **38**

Rank of Alaska, among all states, in the percentage of people who walk to work: **1**

Miles of abandoned U.S. railroad tracks that have been converted to jogging trails: **2,700**

Estimated number of working cabooses in the U.S.: **5,250**

Number of automobiles that have been scrapped in the U.S. since 1946: **288,324,898**

Portion of America's 575,607 bridges that are structurally deficient, obsolete, or closed: **2/5**

Total length of all roads built during the Roman Empire, in miles: **49,000**

Total length of all U.S. interstate highways, in miles: **45,938**

Percentage of Americans who say the automobile is the greatest invention of all time: **10**

Percentage who say the wheel is: **11**

NEW YORK, NEW YORK

Estimated number of people who sleep in Manhattan subway stations: **900**

Purchase price of parking space in New York City's first condominium garage: **$37,000**

Monthly maintenance fee: **$150**

Number of cars abandoned on New York City streets in 1990: **121,041**

Number of corpses found in the Harlem, Hudson, and East rivers in 1989: **49**

Price of a two-hour walking tour of famous murder sites in Manhattan, given by Sidewalks of New York: **$10**

WHAT COUNTS

Number of people killed by stray bullets in New York City in 1989: **39**

Percentage of New York City police officers who fired their guns in the line of duty in 1989: **1.5**

Number of people who died in police custody in New York City in 1989: **30**

Number of New York City police officers who are members of the Screen Actors Guild: **350**

Number of days spent shooting the March 1987 CBS miniseries "I'll Take Manhattan" in New York City: **8**

Number of days spent shooting in Toronto: **75**

Average number of the 35 Broadway theaters that are dark on any given night: **15**

Number of artists-in-residence at the New York City Department of Sanitation: **1**

Percentage of the cargo shipped from the Port of New York that is wastepaper: **30**

Reported cases of people bitten by rats in New York City in 1989: **240**

Reported cases of people bitten by other people: **1,446**

Life span of a sidewalk tree in New York City, in years: **5**

Number of tulip bulbs planted along Park Avenue each year: **100,000**

Number of the 4 wealthiest zip codes in the United States that are on Manhattan's Upper East Side: **3**

Chances that a residential telephone number in New York City is unlisted: **1 in 3**

Average number of people who jump New York City subway turnstiles each minute: **105**

Number of pages of guidelines that the New York City Transit Authority sent to a Boy Scout who wanted to clean a subway station: **6**

Amount of time it takes to ride the entire length of the New York subway system, in hours: **30**

Cab fare from New York City to Los Angeles: **$8,325**

SOUTHERN HOSPITALITY

Number of feet the demographic center of the U.S. population moves to the south each day: **29**

Number of blacks who have moved to the American South since 1980: **1,184,000**

Number who have left the South since 1980: **892,000**

Rank of Texas, among all states, in the number of prisoners executed since 1976: **1**

Number of the 121 executions in the United States since 1977 that occurred outside the South: **11**

Number of people on the waiting list to see an execution in Florida: **100**

Chances that a Southern household owns a gun: **2 in 3**

Percentage increase, since 1987, in the number of children killed by guns in Broward County, Florida: **200**

Rank of Florida, among all states, in the number of people killed by lightning: **1**

Number of states that fly the Confederate flag over their capitol buildings: **2**

Percentage of American Southerners who say they support the Supreme Court's 1973 *Roe* v. *Wade* abortion decision: **45**

Percentage of Texas voters who said in 1987 that they did not consider George Bush "a real Texan": **57**

Maximum fine for holding more than two garage sales per year in Highland Park, Texas: **$1,000**

Percentage of all restaurants in Texas that serve chicken-fried steak: **40**

Ratio of the amount of ice cream consumed by the average Southerner each year to the amount consumed by the average New Englander: **1:2**

Tons of barbecue sold each July 4 at Piggie Park Restaurant in Columbia, South Carolina: **10**

Estimated amount of grease New Orleans restaurants dispose of each year, in gallons: **2,000,000**

Rank of Louisiana, among all states, in the number of professional football players produced per capita: **1**

Maximum fine proposed in 1989 for participating in a dwarf-toss in South Carolina: **$200**

Winning distance in the 1990 guitar-throwing contest held in Baton Rouge, Louisiana, in feet: **89**

AMERICAN PIE

Total amount of land in the United States that is occupied by shopping centers and malls, in acres: **96,738**

Portion of the United States that is inhabited by two or fewer people per square mile: **1/4**

Percentage of Americans who live in mobile homes: **6**

Number of people who attended the ninetieth annual National Hobo Convention in Britt, Iowa, in 1990: **14,000**

Number of feet the demographic center of the U.S. population moves to the west each day: **58**

Rank of "Park," among the most common street names in America: **1**

Rank of "Main": **32**

Chances that a male North Dakotan is an Elk: **1 in 15**

Number of six-fingered Amish dwarfs in Lancaster County, Pennsylvania: **40**

Percentage of Iowans who don't know what *auld lang syne* means: **91**

Average number of Kiwanis Club meetings that take place each day in the United States: **1,012**

Total membership of the Abraham Lincoln Association: **475**

Total membership of the Calvin Coolidge Memorial Foundation: **823**

Percentage of Americans who say that in a democracy, personal freedom is more important than equality: **72**

Number of countries that have claimed to have discovered America: **11**

Number of U.S. cities and towns named Constitution: **4**

Number named Independence: **15**

Number named Moscow: **23**

Rank of blue among Americans' favorite colors: **1**

Number of Elvis impersonators who performed at the centennial of the Statue of Liberty in 1986: **200**

Percentage increase in sales of American flags since 1980: **90**

Percentage of American children under the age of six who say that the first U.S. flag was sewn by Betsy Ross: **15**

Percentage who say that it was sewn by Barbara Bush: **29**

COMMUNICATIONS

NEWS

Rank of the Philippines, Colombia, and Pakistan, among countries where the highest number of journalists was killed in 1990: **1, 2, 3**

Number of pages of his newspaper a Filipino editor says military personnel forced him to eat at gunpoint in 1989: **2**

Number of bulletproof vests *The Washington Post* has bought for its reporters since 1988: **15**

Number of times the phrase *read my lips* appeared in *The Washington Post* during the first two years of George Bush's presidency: **135**

Number of stories on George Bush that aired on the evening network news during his first one hundred days in office: **336**

Number of stories on Jimmy Carter that aired during his first one hundred days: **906**

Percentage change, since 1979, in the average number of hours of television each year devoted to public affairs: **−51**

Rank of Henry Kissinger, Alexander Haig, and Elliott Abrams, among the most frequent guests on "Nightline" between 1985 and 1988: **1, 2, 3**

Rank of Jim and Tammy Faye Bakker's appearance on "Night-line" on May 27, 1987, among the show's most highly rated broadcasts: **1**

Amount of airtime "NBC Nightly News" devoted in August 1990 to an interview with Omar Sharif about U.S.-Arab relations, in seconds: **20**

Maximum amount Ted Turner fines his employees for using the word *foreign* instead of *international* on company time: **$100**

Number of the 33 daily newspapers in New York City that are published in English: **15**

Average number of newspapers and periodicals to which a Soviet family subscribes: **7**

Average number to which an American family subscribes: **4**

Chances that a story in *The Washington Post* or *The New York Times* quotes an unnamed source: **1 in 2**

Percentage of all identified sources quoted in *The New York Times* that are U.S. government officials: **46**

Portion of the Justice Department's public-information staff laid off since George Bush took office: **1/2**

Number of photographs in the Associated Press library that depict President Bush engaged in sports: **108**

Portion of all references to Dan Quayle in *The Washington Post* in 1990 that appeared in the Style section: **1/2**

Portion of network news coverage of the 1988 presidential campaign that focused on the role of television imagery: **1/2**

COMMUNICATIONS

Percentage of Americans who say they don't believe anything that Dan Rather says: **6**

Percentage change, since 1989, in the number of libel suits filed in the United States: **+15**

Number of entries under *journalistic ethics* in the 1961 *Reader's Guide to Periodical Literature*: **0**

Number of entries in the 1990 edition: **24**

Number of times that *New York Times* columnist A. M. Rosenthal's office door was painted in 1987 before he was happy with the color: **4**

THE TUBE

Rank of watching television, among the activities Americans most look forward to during the day: **1**

Percentage of Americans too young to remember life before television: **70**

Chances that an American has appeared on television: **1 in 4**

Percentage of Americans who watch television during dinner: **50**

Rank of coffee, alcohol, and soft drinks, among the foods most often consumed or mentioned on prime-time TV: **1, 2, 3**

WHAT COUNTS

Percentage of Americans who like dogs on television commercials because they are "more exciting than people": **23**

Cost per second of advertising time on "The Simpsons": **$10,000**

Percentage change, since 1980, in the number of Americans who watch prime-time network television: **−25**

Number of network pilots aired in September 1990 in which a character said the word *suck*: **4**

Percentage change, since 1988, in the number of network TV pilots about police officers: **+180**

Average number of murders a viewer witnesses each night on prime-time television: **2**

Average number of pencils and index cards David Letterman tosses over his shoulder during each show: **5**

Rank of sex, crime, and the family, among the topics most frequently discussed on "Geraldo" and "The Oprah Winfrey Show": **1, 2, 3**

Percentage of American men who say they deal with depression by trying to sort out their problems: **23**

Percentage who say they deal with depression by watching television: **35**

Chances that an episode of "Gilligan's Island" is about getting off the island: **1 in 3**

Rank of Marcus Welby and Hawkeye Pierce, among the TV doctors Americans say they would go to if they existed: **1, 2**

COMMUNICATIONS

Percentage of American Jews who say that "All in the Family" is the best sitcom ever: **15**

Percentage of American Protestants who say this: **4**

Portion of the advertisements that were pulled from a 1989 episode of "thirtysomething" in which two homosexuals were shown in bed together: **3/5**

Percentage of the audience of "thirtysomething" who are in their thirties: **31**

Average number of Americans who tape "All My Children" each day: **737,000**

Estimated number of calls received by U.S. soap-opera-update telephone lines each month: **1,000,000**

Number of nations where "Dallas" appears on television: **98**

Estimated number of extramarital affairs that have taken place on "Dallas": **50**

Percentage of the sexual acts depicted or referred to on soap operas that are between married partners: **3**

Average number of sexual innuendos broadcast on television each hour during prime time: **10**

Number of hugs in the final episode of "Family Ties": **20**

Number of shootings in the final episode of "Miami Vice": **40**

HOLLYWOOD

Percentage of Americans who never go to the movies: **32**

Ratio of videocassettes rented to movie tickets purchased in 1990: **6:1**

Number of movie theaters in the United States: **4,532**

Number in the Soviet Union: **150,000**

Number of the 3 highest-grossing foreign films shown in the Soviet Union in 1988 that starred Steve Guttenberg: **2**

Number of the 10 all-time highest-grossing films that were made by Steven Spielberg, George Lucas, or both: **8**

Average amount each member of the Writers Guild of America was paid in residuals in 1989: **$7,148**

Amount the president of the Walt Disney Company was paid in salary, bonuses, and stock options in 1989: **$50,946,000**

Rank of the works of V. I. Lenin and the Walt Disney Company, among those most widely translated worldwide: **1, 2**

Total number of black spots drawn by Disney animators for the movie *101 Dalmatians*: **6,469,952**

Number of rats bred for *Indiana Jones and the Last Crusade*: **3,000**

COMMUNICATIONS

Number of shades of artificial blood sold by Cinema Secrets, a special-effects company in Burbank, California: **6**

Deaths by gunshot in *Scarface*: **41**

Deaths by chain saw: **1**

Percentage of R-rated movies that contain violence: **60**

Percentage of X-rated movies that do: **46**

Rank of *Ferris Bueller's Day Off*, among Dan Quayle's favorite movies: **1**

Number of times George Steinbrenner has seen *Patton*: **15**

Percentage of the feature films made in the United States in 1989 that were shot somewhere other than California: **43**

Portion of the movies Tom Cruise starred in during the 1980s in which he wore sunglasses: **1/2**

Number of Americans killed on screen in *Rambo*: **1**

Number of Vietnamese and Russians killed on screen in *Rambo*: **75**

Number of Rambos in the Washington, D.C., phone book: **3**

Percentage increase in video rentals of *Hoosiers* on the weekend following Dan Quayle's 1988 acceptance speech: **39**

Percentage increase in garter-belt sales at Frederick's of Hollywood in the two months following the release of *Bull Durham*: **50**

Total amount Hollywood antique dealer Malcolm Wilits has received from the sale of fifteen secondhand Oscars: **$170,000**

Number of brand-name products that appear in *Back to the Future, Part II*: **26**

Total ticket sales for the movie *Teenage Mutant Ninja Turtles* in 1990: **$135,000,000**

Total sales of Teenage Mutant Ninja Turtles merchandise in 1990: **$1,865,000,000**

Parking fees that Universal Studios collected in 1988 from people protesting *The Last Temptation of Christ*: **$4,500**

Number of Academy Award recipients in 1989 who thanked God in their acceptance speech: **1**

Number who thanked Hollywood agent Michael Ovitz: **3**

MUSIC

Percentage of Americans who say they often sing, hum, or whistle: **45**

Percentage of Iowans who say that they have a hard time singing "The Star Spangled Banner": **40**

Number of Americans who play the accordion: **2,400,000**

Number of high-school marching bands that have ordered the sheet music for "Barbara Ann" since 1986: **3,233**

Chances that a college freshman has impaired hearing: **3 in 5**

COMMUNICATIONS

Age after which Mick Jagger has said that he'd "rather die" than still be performing "Satisfaction": **45**

Estimated amount Mick Jagger, 46, earned each time he performed "Satisfaction" on the 1989 Rolling Stones tour: **$10,000**

Total number of hours the Grateful Dead has played "Dark Star" in concert: **57**

Number of National Guard officers assigned to monitor a Grateful Dead concert in Foxboro, Massachusetts, in 1990: **40**

Number of blind dates former drug czar William Bennett has had with Janis Joplin: **1**

Percentage of readers of the defunct magazine *Wigwag* who said they knew someone who knew James Taylor: **15**

Percentage of Iowans who say that the death of Sid Vicious affected them personally: **5**

Percentage of the song dedications deejay Casey Kasem reads on the air that he says choke him up: **50**

Number of times WXTB, a Florida radio station, played "Stairway to Heaven" consecutively on December 31, 1989: **181**

Number of different songs broadcast on Muzak's instrumental channel each day: **450**

Percentage increase, since 1985, in the number of all-talk radio stations in the United States: **42**

Ratio of the average salary of a morning radio personality to that of an afternoon radio personality: **3:2**

Number of "golden oldies" radio stations in the United States in 1984: **164**

Number today: **690**

Amount the estate of Elvis Presley earned in 1988: **$15,000,000**

Amount Bon Jovi earned in 1988: **$15,000,000**

Number of times the word *motherfucker* appears in Miles Davis's autobiography: **333**

Number of U.S. colleges that offer an undergraduate degree in jazz: **77**

Percentage of Iowans who say they listen to soul music "fairly often": **13**

Percentage who think that music videos are among the "least useful changes" in modern life: **67**

Rank of *love*, *baby*, and *time*, among the nouns used most frequently in Madonna's songs: **1, 2, 3**

Rank of *night*, *girl*, and *street*, among the nouns used most frequently in Bruce Springsteen's songs: **1, 2, 3**

Number of requests for 2 Live Crew lyric sheets received by the Parents' Music Resource Center in 1990: **1,500**

Number of requests for New Kids on the Block lyric sheets: **3,000**

Number of hours it took Jennifer Norwood of the PMRC to transcribe the lyrics of 2 Live Crew's album *As Nasty as They Wanna Be*: **9**

COMMUNICATIONS

Number of record-store clerks arrested in the United States since 1986 on obscenity charges for selling certain albums to minors: **4**

Percentage of American teenagers who say that their favorite songs are about sex, violence, satanism, or drugs: **7**

Percentage who say that they are about love: **26**

Percentage who say they don't know what their favorite songs are about: **37**

READING AND WRITING

Percentage increase, since 1988, in the number of periodicals seized or banned worldwide: **121**

Estimated amount Viking Penguin earned from the sales of Salman Rushdie's *The Satanic Verses* in its first year of publication: **$3,400,000**

Estimated amount Viking Penguin spent on extra security that year: **$3,400,000**

Copies of Gabriel García Márquez's *Clandestine in Chile* that were burned by the Chilean government in 1986: **15,000**

Copies of George Orwell's *1984* sold each day in the United States in 1984: **3,500**

Number of years that George Bush cited Tom Wolfe's *The*

Bonfire of the Vanities as an example of his current pleasure reading: **2**

Rank of celebrities, politicians, and family members, among the people mentioned most often in Nancy Reagan's memoirs: **1, 2, 3**

Number of times Tammy Faye Bakker mentions crying in her two books *I Gotta Be Me* and *Run to the Roar*: **60**

Number of times the term *S.O.B.* appears in *Confessions of an S.O.B.*, the autobiography of former Gannett chairman Al Neuharth: **92**

Percentage of Americans over the age of fifty who say they read a daily newspaper: **65**

Percentage of Americans under the age of thirty who say they do: **40**

Number of American adults who read below the eighth-grade level: **36,000,000**

Rank of *innovative*, *gregarious*, and *indulge*, among the vocabulary words that appear most frequently on the SAT: **1, 2, 3**

Rank of "dog," "cat," "snake," "horse," and "U.S. President," among *World Book Encyclopedia* entries most often consulted by students: **1, 2, 3, 4, 5**

Number of words in the English language that exist because of typographical errors or misreadings: **381**

Average number of words added to the English language each year: **450**

COMMUNICATIONS

Number of documented expressions in English for being drunk: **2,500**

Length of the entry for the word *set* in the 1989 edition of the *Oxford English Dictionary,* in pages: **60**

Percentage of book reviewers who say it is ethical to review a book without having finished it: **36**

Number of times Rod McKuen says he rewrote his book *The Sound of Solitude*: **34**

Number of romance novels published each month in the United States: **120**

Minimum cost of a personalized romance novel from Swan Publishing of Placentia, California: **$45**

Rank of *Cosmopolitan, Glamour,* and *Vogue,* among the best-selling magazines in college bookstores: **1, 2, 3**

Rank of acting, happiness, and modeling, among the ambitions most often cited by *Playboy* centerfold models: **1, 2, 3**

Number of times the word *fuck* appears in *Nails,* the autobiography of former New York Met Lenny Dykstra: **160**

Number of exclamation points in Tom Wolfe's *The Bonfire of the Vanities*: **2,343**

Total number of weeks since December 1981 that Danielle Steel has not had a book on a national best-seller list: **10**

Chances that a monkey with a typewriter will type Hamlet: **1 in $35^{200,000}$**

Chances that a monkey with a typewriter will type *Bright Lights, Big City*: **1 in $35^{300,000}$**

IN THE MAIL

Average annual increase, since 1980, in the amount of junk mail an American receives, in pounds: **15.7**

Number of Americans who have requested that their names be removed from direct-mail marketing lists since 1985: **1,040,000**

Estimated number of direct-mail solicitations sent to Henry David Thoreau at Walden Pond each month: **25**

Estimated number of valentines mailed to Elvis Presley at Graceland each year: **100**

Average number of greeting cards an American receives each year: **30**

Percentage of Americans who buy humorous greeting cards who say they think of themselves as funny: **74**

Percentage of Americans who say they have been "moved to tears" by a greeting card: **29**

Pieces of mail that end up in the U.S. Postal Service's dead-letter office each year: **57,100,000**

Percentage of first-class domestic mail that is delivered on time, according to the U.S. Postal Service: **94**

COMMUNICATIONS

Chances that a post-office employee in New York City has failed a drug test: **1 in 3**

Estimated number of wallets found by postal workers in Manhattan mail-collection boxes each day: **200**

Amount the U.S. Postal Service spent in 1989 to maintain mules to deliver mail in the Grand Canyon: **$156,165**

Average number of mail carriers bitten by dogs each day: **9**

ON THE PHONE

Rank of the day after the 1989 San Francisco earthquake, among days on which the greatest number of long-distance calls were made: **1**

Estimated total value of the illegal long-distance telephone calls made in the United States each year: **$500,000,000**

Estimated percentage change in local telephone rates since the breakup of AT&T: **+60**

Number of information operators on duty weeknights at 2:00 A.M. in Mississippi: **2**

Number on duty weeknights at 2:00 A.M. in New York City: **17**

Percentage of international telephone conversations that are conducted in English: **85**

WHAT COUNTS

Estimated waiting period in 1990 for a telephone in Poland, in years: **20**

Number of the 15 fax machines in the Gaza Strip whose use the Israeli government has banned: **15**

Number of injuries in the United States in 1989 attributed to "telephones or telephone accessories": **12,953**

Number of times George Bush telephoned Gloria Estéfan during her stay in the hospital in 1990: **3**

Number of people who try unsuccessfully to get George Bush on the telephone each year: **250,000**

Number of times Marion Barry used his car phone to call alleged drug connections during his last four years in office: **2,312**

Number of public telephones Southwestern Bell installed in 1990 that can be used while on horseback: **3**

Number that can be used while seated in a golf cart: **1**

ECONOMICS

▬▀▬▀▬▀▬▀▬▀▬▀▬▀▬▀▬▀▬▀▬▀▬▀▬▀▬

Wealth and Poverty

Taxes

IOUs

Imports and Exports

High Finance

Corporate America

The Labor Force

On the Job

Shopping

Price Tags

WEALTH AND POVERTY

Average earnings of each of the ten most prosperous Wall Street professionals in 1990: **$61,000,000**

Chances that an American family doesn't have a bank account: **1 in 5**

Percentage of Americans who say they daydream about being rich: **49**

Percentage of all private wealth in the United States that was held by the richest half-percent of Americans in 1976: **14**

Percentage held by the richest half-percent in 1986. **24**

Average change, since 1977, in the annual federal taxes paid by the richest 1 percent of American families: **−$45,142**

Average change in the annual federal taxes paid by the remaining 99 percent: **+$161**

Percentage of American families living below the poverty line in which at least one member is employed: **63**

Percentage of Americans who believe hard work is the way people get rich: **43**

Percentage of the four hundred richest Americans who inherited their wealth: **23**

Number of countries that have a lower infant mortality rate than the United States: **18**

Percentage of black children in the United States who live below the poverty line: **46**

Number of soup kitchens in New York City in 1981: **30**

Number in 1990: **700**

Cost of an annual corporate membership in the Breakfast Club at New York's "21" Club: **$6,500**

Percentage of American men earning seventy thousand dollars a year or more who say they cheat on their wives: **70**

Percentage earning less than five thousand dollars a year who say they do: **16**

Percentage of Americans who believe "differences in social standing reflect what people have made of their opportunities": **72**

Chances that a homeless American holds a full- or part-time job: **1 in 3**

Chances that an American earning hourly wages is paid less than five dollars an hour: **1 in 4**

Percentage of American families whose net worth is less than ten thousand dollars: **25**

Percentage increase, since 1978, in the number of American

households reporting incomes of over one million dollars a year: **3,000**

Number of the world's 182 billionaires who are not American: **124**

Percentage change, since 1980, in U.S. sales of stretch limousines: **+130**

Number of hand-carved marble columns in the living room of Donald Trump's Trump Tower triplex: **29**

Amount Michael Milken earned in 1987: **$550,000,000**

Estimated 1927 gross income of Al Capone, in 1987 dollars: **$600,000,000**

TAXES

Hours after the 1991 tax increase was passed that President Bush promised to "hold the line on taxes" from now on: **13**

Average portion of their tax dollars that Americans say are wasted: **1/2**

Average number of minutes of each workday that an American spends earning money to pay taxes: **165**

Number of states that require a family of four living below the poverty level to pay income taxes: **25**

Number of Americans who declared more than $200,000 in income and paid no federal taxes in 1989: **595**

Number of the top 6 military contractors that have paid less than 10 percent of their total earnings in federal income tax since 1981: **3**

Percentage of the federal income taxes paid by individuals in 1980 that went to military programs: **45**

Percentage in 1990 that did: **50**

Tax revenues that Oklahoma gains each time the price of a barrel of oil rises a dollar: **$7,924,405**

Percentage of U.S. taxpayers who pay more in Social Security tax than in federal income tax: **38**

Percentage by which the 1990 U.S. budget deficit would have increased if Social Security surplus funds had not been counted as revenue: **26**

Additional hours Americans spend on paperwork each year as a result of the 1986 tax reform legislation: **525,000,000**

Estimated number of documents the IRS loses each year: **2,000,000**

Total amount of time each year that Americans spend on hold while calling the IRS, in years: **35**

Number of times a year that the IRS telephones its own tax-help line to check its quality: **15,000**

Chances that a caller to the IRS tax-help line will be given inaccurate information: **1 in 4**

Estimated gallons of ink used at H&R Block offices during the tax season: **16**

Estimated gallons of coffee used: **2,200,000**

IOUs

Estimated amount the U.S. national debt will increase in the time it takes to read this line: **$33,000**

Number of years since the balanced-budget law went into effect in 1985 that its deficit-reduction targets have been met: **0**

Net foreign debt owed to U.S. government, businesses, and citizens in 1981, per American family: **$2,500**

Net foreign debt owed by U.S. government, businesses, and citizens in 1989, per American family: **$20,114**

Percentage of U.S. households that pay their bills exclusively in cash: **15**

Total outstanding balance on U.S. credit cards at the end of 1980: **$54,894,000,000**

Total outstanding balance on U.S. credit cards at the end of 1989: **$201,801,000,000**

Percentage of Americans who say "the bad effects of credit cards outweigh the good": **45**

Number of years it would take to pay off the U.S. national debt at the rate of ten thousand dollars per minute: **615**

Ratio of the number of corporate bonds that Moody's downgraded in 1990 to the number it upgraded: **4:1**

Ratio in 1984: **1:1**

Percentage of the 1990 pretax profits of U.S. companies that went to interest payments: **57**

Ratio of U.S. corporate assets to liabilities in 1980: **4:1**

Ratio in 1989: **2:1**

Percentage of the 1990 federal budget that was spent on debt service: **21**

Ratio of IMF-member countries operating with a deficit to those operating with a surplus: **5:2**

Estimated increase in Latin America's debt burden each time U.S. interest rates increase 1 percent: **$500,000,000**

Acres of wilderness Bolivia agreed to preserve in 1987 in exchange for a $650,000 reduction in its foreign debt: **2,700,000**

Pounds of frozen chicken that Peru exported to the Soviet Union in 1985 to help pay back a loan: **1,860,432**

IMPORTS AND EXPORTS

Rank of IBM, among the leading computer export firms in Japan: **1**

ECONOMICS

Portion of all U.S. imports that are produced by American companies abroad: **1/5**

Percentage of U.S. overseas development aid in 1988 that was tied to the purchase of American goods: **51**

Percentage of Japanese overseas development aid in 1988 that was tied to the purchase of Japanese goods: **24**

Percentage of the cars Chrysler sold in the United States in 1989 that were manufactured overseas: **10**

Percentage of Japanese cars sold in the United States in 1989 that were manufactured here: **28**

Percentage increase in the amount of cargo shipped between Asia and the United States since 1983: **107**

Amount spent by Americans in 1989 on adoption fees for Korean babies: **$21,312,000**

Amount spent by South Korea in 1989 for American waste-paper: **$138,800,000**

Percentage of South Korea's gross national product accounted for by export earnings: **29**

Percentage of Japan's gross national product accounted for by export earnings: **10**

Ratio of Japanese cars sold in the United States to German cars sold in the United States in 1990: **8:1**

Ratio of German cars sold in Japan to American cars sold in Japan in 1990: **8:1**

Portion of all world exports in 1989 that went to the United States: **1/5**

WHAT COUNTS

Percentage of California's almond crop exported to Japan and Europe each year: **58**

Rank of aircraft, computer equipment, and wood, among the United States' leading exports to Japan in 1989: **1, 2, 3**

Rank of vehicles, office equipment, and audio and video recorders, among Japan's leading exports to the United States in 1989: **1, 2, 3**

Value of the South African iron and steel the United States has imported since Congress imposed sanctions in 1986: **$599,519,000**

Amount added to South Africa's annual export earnings by every ten-dollar increase in the price of gold: **$194,915,520**

Percentage of all Tiffany & Co. shopping bags that are manufactured in El Salvador: **75**

Percentage of Nicaragua's exports that were bought by Japan in 1985: **25**

Percentage in 1989: **6**

Total value of U.S. exports to China in the five months following the Tiananmen Square massacre: **$2,215,100,000**

Percentage increase in trade between China and the Soviet Union since 1981: **533**

Percentage of the manhole covers imported by the United States that are made in India: **56**

Estimated percentage of the U.S. pencil market supplied by domestic manufacturers: **95**

HIGH FINANCE

Portion of all corporate bonds currently outstanding in the United States that are junk bonds: **1/4**

Percentage decrease, since 1989, in the combined annual worth of new junk bond issues: **94**

Number of the U.S. companies financed with junk bonds that failed to meet loan obligations in 1990: **32**

Percentage of all outstanding junk bonds that are owned by U.S. life insurance companies: **17**

Portion of the 130 U.S. life insurance company insolvencies since 1975 that took place during the last five years: **1/2**

Number of U.S. banks classified as "problems" by the FDIC: **1,034**

Percentage of U.S. savings-and-loan institutions that failed during the Depression: **5**

Percentage that the government expects to fail by 1995: **25**

Projected total cost to taxpayers of the S&L bailout, expressed as a percentage of the federal deficit: **300**

Estimated net amount the S&L bailout will cost the North-eastern states: **$41,900,000,000**

Estimated net amount the Sunbelt states will receive as a result of the bailout: **$110,700,000,000**

Estimated portion of U.S. S&L insolvencies in 1990 that resulted from "criminal fraud": **1/3**

Rank of the Resolution Trust Corporation, which manages the S&L bailout, among the largest U.S. real-estate concerns: **1**

Rank of the Resolution Trust Corporation, among the largest U.S. financial institutions: **1**

Percentage of the world's total stock-market capital accounted for by shares of U.S. corporations: **35**

Percentage accounted for by shares of Japanese corporations: **40**

Percentage of Chrysler's 1989 profits that came from the sale of Mitsubishi stock: **86**

Percentage change, since 1989, in foreign investment in U.S. stocks, bonds, and Treasury securities: **−80**

Percentage change, since 1989, in U.S. investment in foreign stocks and bonds: **+68**

Estimated amount by which the value of stock taken off the market due to mergers and acquisitions exceeded that of new stock issued in 1989: **$124,200,000**

Percentage of individual U.S. investors who did not sell any stock in the two weeks following the October 1987 crash: **87**

Percentage increase, since 1980, in the average number of

shares traded each day on the New York Stock Exchange: **250**

Percentage change, since 1987, in the cost of a seat on the New York Stock Exchange: **−38**

Rank of U.S. stock markets, among markets worldwide, in percentage gain since 1982: **14**

Number of the world's 25 largest banks that are Japanese: **17**

Number that are American: **1**

Estimated amount stolen from federally insured financial institutions by armed bank robbers in 1989: **$1,000,000,000**

Estimated amount stolen through bank fraud and embezzlement: **$1,300,000,000**

CORPORATE AMERICA

Portion of all M.B.A.'s ever awarded by U.S. universities that were awarded during the 1980s: **1/2**

Chances that a merger involving U.S. companies will be hostile: **1 in 4**

Chances that a corporate merger in 1980 was challenged by the federal government: **1 in 222**

Chances that a corporate merger in 1989 was challenged: **1 in 487**

WHAT COUNTS

Average number of U.S. companies that filed for bankruptcy each day in 1989: **173**

Number of jobs added to the economy by the Fortune 500 since 1980: **0**

Number of Fortune 500 companies whose personnel departments have employed genetic screening or monitoring: **20**

Percentage of U.S. companies that have a policy against hiring smokers: **4**

Percentage of American CEOs who say they would "hesitate" to promote a homosexual to an executive position: **66**

Chances that a female executive has never married: **1 in 5**

Percentage of female executives over the age of forty who have children: **39**

Percentage of male executives over the age of forty who do: **96**

Percentage of American CEOs who have served in the armed forces: **75**

Portion of the top 250 U.S. industrial companies that had "golden parachute" plans for their executives in 1982: **1/5**

Portion that had such plans in 1989: **1/2**

Number of shares of stock in their own companies that oil- and gas-industry executives sold between August and December 1990: **1,130,000**

Average change, in 1988, in the top executive's salary at

companies that laid off at least one thousand workers:
+$174,000

Average hourly rate Chrysler paid CEO Lee Iacocca in 1989:
$1,921.29

Average hourly wage of an American autoworker in 1989:
$15.74

Average percentage change, since 1989, in the square footage
of a corporate vice-president's office: −25

Percentage increase, since 1986, in the total amount of paper
consumed by U.S. businesses each year: 100

Amount Drexel Burnham Lambert spent in 1988 copying
documents requested by the SEC for its investigation:
$46,000,000

Value of the year-end bonuses that Drexel gave its employees
in 1989: $270,000,000

Estimated amount the company requested in bank loans before
it filed for bankruptcy in February 1990: $300,000,000

Total salary Drexel paid two of its financial analysts in the
year after it declared bankruptcy: $1,933,332

Cost to the U.S. Treasury of business deductions for meals
and entertainment in 1989: $8,200,000,000

Number of country-club memberships RJR Nabisco purchased
in 1988 for Ross Johnson, its CEO: 24

Percentage of the board members of Fortune 1000 companies
who are white males: 92

Percentage of female executives who say that wearing perfume helps a woman's career: **36**

THE LABOR FORCE

Ratio of the averge American CEO's salary to that of a blue-collar worker in 1991: **91:1**

Ratio in 1980: **25:1**

Number of years since 1980 in which increases in blue-collar wages have failed to keep up with inflation: **8**

Average salary and benefits of workers in U.S. industries in which the number of jobs is decreasing: **$32,000**

Average salary and benefits in industries in which the number of jobs is increasing: **$22,000**

Percentage of the new jobs created since 1979 that were filled by women: **64**

Percentage increase, since 1978, in the number of U.S. firms that offer child-care benefits: **1,696**

Percentage of the members of the AFL-CIO who are women: **32**

Number of the 35 members of the AFL-CIO executive council who are women: **3**

Change, between 1988 and 1989, in the total number of manufacturing jobs in the United States: **+260,000**

Change in the number of these jobs held by union members: **−47,000**

Percentage decrease, since 1980, in the number of labor strikes in the United States: **73**

Chances, in 1970, that a U.S. company would continue to operate despite a strike: **1 in 10**

Chances today: **3 in 4**

Number of jobs filled each day in the United States by temporary workers: **1,031,500**

Percentage increase, since 1979, in the number of Americans unemployed for longer than six months: **21**

Percentage of unemployed Americans who receive no unemployment benefits: **67**

Average number of annual paid vacation days for an American worker: **9**

Minimum number of paid vacation days, after one year of service, for a German worker: **30**

Average increase, since 1973, in the number of hours an employed American works each week: **6.2**

Percentage increase, since 1985, in the number of fines imposed in the United States for child-labor-law violations: **128**

Average number of workplace safety violations found in each inspection by the Occupational Safety and Health Administration: **4**

ON THE JOB

Number of Americans who are monitored at work by computer: **6,000,000**

Number of Americans who were given a drug urinalysis test on the job in 1990: **10,000,000**

Estimated number of Americans who are fired each workday: **11,800**

Average number of jobs an American worker has held by age forty: **8**

Chances that an employed American works in a shopping center or mall: **1 in 11**

Percentage of Americans who believe their occupation is fulfilling or exciting: **67**

Percentage of fast-food-restaurant employees who say they have stolen food or money from their employer: **62**

Percentage who admit to doing "slow, sloppy work on purpose": **22**

Chances that a private-sector work-related illness reported in 1988 was caused by repetitive motion disorder: **1 in 2**

ECONOMICS

Number of workdays lost each year because of headaches: **157,000,000**

Percentage of Americans who say that Monday is their favorite day of the week: **3**

Percentage who say they want their boss's job: **29**

Average number of miles walked on the job each year by a factory worker: **2,227**

Average number walked by a housewife: **594**

Daily wage a French company paid American workers in 1988 to pick sprayed crops to test the effects of a new pesticide on humans: **$100**

Chances that a New York City traffic officer will be physically assaulted on the job this year: **1 in 12**

Chances that a firefighter's meal on the job will be interrupted: **3 in 5**

Number of Census Bureau employees who have been bitten by people they were trying to count: **1**

SHOPPING

Percentage of American adults who say they have been to a shopping center in the last month: **94**

Ratio of square feet of shopping center built to the number of babies born in the United States since 1986: **40:1**

Estimated value of goods purchased by Americans through TV shopping channels in 1990: **$1,900,000,000**

Portion of consumer purchases in the United States that are paid for in cash: **1/3**

Number of different clothing colors featured in the fall 1990 Tweeds catalog: **125**

Chances that a man is accompanied by a woman when he shops for clothes: **2 in 3**

Rank of shopping for clothes, among American women's favorite shopping trips: **1**

Rank of shopping for a car, among American men's favorite shopping trips: **1**

Average number of people a satisfied car owner tells about his or her car: **8**

Average number a dissatisfied car owner tells: **22**

Total amount consumers pay for food packaging each year: **$55,000,000,000**

Average number of different items in a grocery store's produce section in 1975: **65**

Average number today: **240**

Percentage of supermarket buying decisions that are made in the store: **65**

Percentage of supermarket prices that end in the digit 9 or 5:
80

PRICE TAGS

Price of having a human body mummified by the Summum
company of Salt Lake City: **$23,700**

Price of storing a unit of blood for one month at Bloodline,
Inc., of Florham Park, New Jersey: **$5**

Average price of an artificial blood vessel in the United States:
$315

Average price of an electronic artificial arm: **$50,000**

Price of a Jane Fonda workout videocassette on the black
market in Moscow: **$372**

Price of a condom on the black market in Moscow: **$10**

Price of a 0.5-cc unit of human semen in the United States:
$85

Average price of a 0.5-cc unit of Holstein bull semen: **$25**

Highest price ever paid for a cow at auction: **$1,300,000**

Price of renting a giant panda from the Chinese government
in 1988, per day: **$1,500**

Average price of a twenty-five-foot epoxy-and-fiberglass banyan tree for a zoo aviary from the Larson Company of Tucson, Arizona: **$110,000**

Price of painting a dried-out lawn green, from Landscape Services of Santa Barbara, California, per one thousand square feet: **$125**

Price of leasing one New York State sugar maple tree for a single sap season: **$39.95**

Average price of a pheasant at Lobel's Prime Meats in New York City: **$52.50**

Price of a one-pound bag of "party ice cubes," cut from Alaskan icebergs, from Northland Service in Juneau: **$1.50**

Suggested retail price of a ten-ounce bottle of Mendocino Truffle Mineral Water: **$1.75**

Price of a one-day seminar on manners taught by Letitia Baldridge: **$6,000**

Price of a two-hour Scandal Tour of Washington, D.C.: **$27**

Price of a set of "RN" golf balls from the gift shop at the Nixon Library and Birthplace in Yorba Linda, California: **$6**

Price that the Bible President Reagan sent to Iran in 1987 would have sold for at auction that year, according to Sotheby's: **$100,000**

Price a paper shredder owned by Drexel Burnham Lambert was sold for at an auction of the company's assets in 1990: **$450**

Net worth of Donald Trump in 1990, per pound: **$9,700,000**

SCIENCE

Technology

Outer Space

Weather Conditions

Reaping and Sowing

The Animal Kingdom

The Environment

Energy

Health Risks

Health Care

The AIDS Virus

TECHNOLOGY

Number of Americans who have been killed on the job by a robot: **2**

Ratio of Japan's robot population to that of the United States: **4:1**

Estimated percentage of Japan's corporate R&D that is funded by the government each year: **1.7**

Estimated percentage of the United States' corporate R&D that is: **33**

Portion of all university funding for computer-science research that comes from the Pentagon: **2/3**

Estimated number of antiviral computer programs on the market: **20**

Prize offered in 1989 by Japan's telephone company to any computer hacker who could penetrate its security system: **$7,700**

Average percentage change in the amount of time an American household spends watching TV after the acquisition of a personal computer: **−40**

WHAT COUNTS

Price of Dr. Cloner's Genetic Engineering Home Clone Kit, for "children over twelve," from Genemsco Corporation of Kingston, Massachusetts: **$559**

Number of geep, genetically engineered composites of goats and sheep, that have been created at the University of California at Davis: **14**

Portion of the 403 U.S. biotechnology companies that use human tissue for commercial research: **1/3**

Percentage of U.S. hospitals that have applied for patents on inventions that use human tissues and cells: **50**

Payment that five former employees demanded from Du Pont in 1988 in return for keeping the formula for Lycra a secret: **$10,000,000**

Amount Du Pont has contributed to the National Plastic Museum in Leominster, Massachusetts: **$50,000**

Number of the 26 human bodies frozen in the hope of being brought back to life that are in California: **24**

Estimated yield in 2090 of a hundred-thousand-dollar Individual Reanimation Account established by a cryogenic-suspension candidate today: **$219,976,130**

Estimated percentage of all the scientists who have ever lived who are alive today: **85**

Decimal places to which the value of pi has been calculated: **134,217,700**

Estimated number of scientific and technical articles published each day, worldwide, in 1990: **24,000**

SCIENCE

Average number of suggestions for new ways to use Velcro that are made each week to Velcro USA: **4**

Number of veterinary operations assisted in 1990 by Robodoc, a surgical robot: **15**

Number of Americans who have someone else's heart: **5,800**

OUTER SPACE

Chances that an American believes that "there are people somewhat like ourselves living on other planets in the universe": **1 in 2**

Percentage of Americans who didn't attend college who say they believe in extraterrestrials: **37**

Percentage of Americans who did attend college who say this: **47**

Members of the International Flat Earth Research Society: **3,500**

Number of people who have been in orbit: **231**

Percentage of American astronauts who have experienced motion sickness in space: **53**

Number of seconds added to 1989 to accommodate a decrease in the earth's rotational speed: **1**

Number of elementary particles in the observable universe: 10^{80}

Number of sightings of a triangular UFO reported in southern Belgium in 1989: **2,600**

Percentage of Iowans who say they didn't try to see Halley's Comet in 1986: **74**

Total sales of products tied to Halley's Comet since then: **$500,000,000**

Percentage of Americans who were born after *Sputnik* was launched in 1957: **50**

Number of the 16,064 Soviet-made objects orbiting the earth that are debris: **13,446**

Number of the 7,283 U.S.-made objects orbiting the earth that are debris: **6,127**

Chances that a space shuttle will crash within the next four years, assuming all systems are 98 percent reliable, according to NASA: **1 in 2**

Pounds of toxic chemicals released during each space-shuttle launch: **77,600**

Total incentive awards NASA had paid the manufacturer of the Hubble space-telescope mirror before it was found to be defective: **$11,000,000**

Estimated distance Dan Quayle discounted when describing Mars as "somewhat the same distance from the sun" as earth is, in miles: **48,600,000**

Diameter of the earth if it were compressed to the density of a black hole, in inches: **7/10**

WEATHER CONDITIONS

Percentage increase in the heat of the sun during the last 3.5 billion years: **25**

Number of the seven hottest years in this century that have occurred since 1980: **6**

Percentage of Iowans who say it's not the heat, it's the humidity: **87**

Estimated increase, since 1982, in the temperature of the Atlantic Ocean: **1°F**

Percentage of Americans who believe that rocket launches have caused changes in the weather: **44**

Bolts of lightning that strike the United States each day: **250,000**

Number of Americans struck by lightning in 1985: **350**

Number struck by lightning in 1989: **700**

Average number of Americans who freeze to death each year: **700**

Chances of a white Christmas in New York City: **1 in 4**

Chances in Minneapolis: **3 in 4**

Rank of 1989, among the last twenty years with the least amount of snow cover in the Northern Hemisphere: **1**

Number of snowflakes that have ever fallen on earth: 10^{35}

Percentage of all the salt produced in the United States that is used to melt ice on roads: **42**

Cost of making a cubic foot of snow: **2¢**

Percentage of Americans who say that spring fever makes them sad: **4**

Rank of May, among all months, in the number of tornadoes in the United States: **1**

Portion of the annual U.S. rainfall that falls in April: **1/12**

Estimated rate at which rain would have to fall to re-create the flood described in Genesis, in feet per hour: **15**

Industry estimate of the life span of an umbrella, in months: **18**

REAPING AND SOWING

Estimated number of the world's 75,000 edible plant species that humans have ever cultivated: **7,000**

Number of weed species that have developed a resistance to herbicides since 1968: **81**

SCIENCE

Ratio of tons of grain produced to tons of fertilizer used world-wide in 1950: **44:1**

Ratio today: **13:1**

Pounds of pesticide produced in the United States each year, per capita: **4.5**

Percentage of the insecticide used in the United States each year that actually reaches a targeted insect: **0.003**

Number of people worldwide who die each year as a result of pesticide poisoning: **14,000**

Chances that an Iowan's drinking water contains traces of one or more pesticides: **1 in 7**

Chances that an acre of U.S. cropland was insured against drought in 1989: **2 in 5**

Chances that the U.S. government paid the premiums: **1 in 4**

Estimated percentage of the total 1991 U.S. farm income that will come from the federal government: **31**

Ratio of the number of foreclosures initiated by the Farmers Home Administration in 1990 to the number initiated in 1989: **5:1**

Percentage of all U.S. cropland that the government pays farmers not to plant each year: **17**

Percentage change, since 1979, in the number of harvest combines sold in the United States: **−81**

Number of farming magazines published in 1974: **209**

Number published today: **322**

Percentage of all water used by humans worldwide that is used for irrigation: **70**

Average net earnings per acre of farmland in Iowa: **$60**

Average net earnings per acre of farmland in Massachusetts: **$305**

Total number of acres in the United States that are occupied by home vegetable gardens: **1,300,000**

Percentage of backyard gardeners who grow tomatoes: **85**

Percentage who grow parsnips: **5**

Largest pumpkin ever grown, in pounds: **755**

Number of four-leaf-clover farms in the United States: **1**

Average amount of gas a cow belches each day, in cubic feet: **35**

THE ANIMAL KINGDOM

Number of new animals and plants that have been patented since 1980: **2,632**

Number of animal species into which a human gene has been introduced: **16**

SCIENCE

Number of animals that animal-rights activists have freed from U.S. research laboratories since 1985: **3,481**

Number of snails that activists liberated from a snail farm in England in 1989: **153,000**

Number of pairs of Wellington boots for cows sold by the Gates Rubber Company of Dumfries, Scotland, since they were introduced in 1989: **3,000**

Number of curbside frog ramps in the streets of Stevens Point, Wisconsin: **4**

Number of alligator farms in the United States: **170**

Average number of live male chicks the U.S. egg industry discards each day: **667,000**

Number of wild turkeys in the United States in 1940: **20,000**

Number today: **2,500,000**

Estimated number of bald eagles that have died as a result of the *Exxon Valdez* oil spill: **144**

Number of rhinoceroses killed by poachers in Zimbabwe in 1990: **27**

Number of alleged rhinoceros poachers killed: **34**

Estimated number of plant and animal species that have become extinct since 1980: **100,000**

Percentage of all plant and animal species known to have ever existed that exist today: **0.01**

Percentage of all animal species worldwide that are beetles: **40**

Estimated percentage of insect species worldwide that have not yet been identified: **90**

Ratio of the total weight of the earth's human population to that of its termite population: **1:10**

Number of muscles in an elephant's trunk: **100,000**

Average weight of a male black bear in Pennsylvania, in pounds: **325**

Average weight of a male polar bear in Alaska, in pounds: **1,000**

Average percentage of a bear's weight that is lost during hibernation: **25**

Percentage change, since 1966, in the U.S. blue jay population: **−34**

Number of bird species that have been sighted in New York City's Central Park since its opening in 1858: **269**

Number of blossoms required to provide a hummingbird with its daily nectar: **1,600**

Number of bees that invaded a Bayport, New York, home in 1990 while the owners were on vacation: **20,000**

Estimated amount of honey they produced before being removed, in pounds: **10**

Number of insect and related species that were resistant to pesticides in 1970: **224**

Number that are today: **504**

SCIENCE

Number of days an ant can survive underwater: **14**

Life expectancy of a worker ant, in months: **3**

Life span of an adult mayfly, in days: **1**

THE ENVIRONMENT

Number of countries that have an environmental protection agency: **161**

Number that had one in 1972: **26**

Percentage of Americans who consider themselves environmentalists: **76**

Average number of acres of land purchased for national parks during the Carter administration, per day: **287**

Average number of acres purchased during the Reagan administration, per day: **78**

Average number of acres of rain forest cut down each day in the United States: **286**

Percentage change in acres of forest in New York State over the last hundred years: **+164**

Number of trees Harper & Row has planted to replace those used in 1990 to publish *2 Minutes a Day for a Greener Planet*: **1,000**

Estimated portion of carbon-dioxide emissions worldwide that is the result of deforestation: **1/4**

Estimated portion of chlorofluorocarbon production worldwide that comes from Du Pont: **1/4**

Total amount of styrofoam waste generated by McDonald's in the United States since the chain started using such packaging, in cubic feet: **24,000,000,000**

Total volume of the World Trade Center towers in New York City, in cubic feet: **54,000,000**

Estimated average number of styrofoam cups an American discards each year: **100**

Portion of all garbage discarded by Americans that is packaging: **1/3**

Average increase, since 1980, in the amount of garbage an American discards each year, in pounds: **69**

Pounds of hazardous waste produced in the United States each year, per capita: **2,600**

Number of the chemicals used to make plastic that rank among the 6 leading producers of hazardous waste: **5**

Number of U.S. states that dispose of toxic waste in another state: **50**

Percentage of Americans who live in areas where the air does not meet the standards of the 1970 Clean Air Act: **60**

Number of the 1,077 toxic-waste sites the EPA Superfund targeted for cleanup in 1981 that remained hazardous in 1989: **1,047**

Portion of all nuclear-plant waste that the Nuclear Regulatory Commission considers "below regulatory concern": **1/2**

Ratio of the amount of hazardous waste produced by the Pentagon to that produced by the top three industrial-waste-producing private U.S. companies: **2:1**

Amount of industrial chemicals legally released into U.S. waters each year, according to the EPA, in pounds: **9,700,000,000**

Estimated percentage of the oil spilled by the *Exxon Valdez* in 1988 that has been recovered from the environment: **8**

Number of nuclear reactors abandoned in the world's oceans: **8**

Gallons of poison the New York State Department of Environmental Conservation dumped into ponds and lakes in 1990 in order to kill fish that displace trout: **810**

Portion of all U.S. coastal waters that are too polluted for commercial shellfishing: **1/3**

Chances that the level of pollution in a U.S. river has grown worse or not improved since 1970: **9 in 10**

Chances that a rural Salvadoran had access to safe drinking water in 1980: **2 in 5**

Chances today: **1 in 5**

Portion of all fresh water in Poland that is too polluted for industrial use: **1/2**

Percentage of the U.S. hazardous waste shipped abroad in 1989 that went to Canada: **75**

Amount that was offered to the Congo in 1988 to accept one hundred thousand tons of Europe's toxic waste: **$7,063,500**

Percentage of Africa that is wilderness: **28**

Percentage of North America that is: **38**

Pounds of trash retrieved from Mount Everest in 1990: **2,000**

Amount of trash left in New York City's Central Park by people attending festivities marking the twentieth anniversary of Earth Day, in tons: **100**

ENERGY

Chances that one of the 114 operating U.S. nuclear reactors will melt down in the next twenty years: **1 in 8**

Average number of emergency shutdowns each year at a U.S. nuclear power plant: **6**

Percentage of Americans who say the "bad effects of nuclear energy outweigh the good": **36**

Number of Soviets who still live in areas contaminated by the Chernobyl accident: **2,200,200**

Percentage of the Department of Energy's 1991 research budget that it proposed to spend on defense: **42**

Change, since 1985, in the percentage of U.S. oil imports that come from Mexico, Canada, and Britain: **− 11**

Change, since 1985, in the percentage of U.S. oil imports that come from Arab countries: **+5**

Percentage of U.S. electrical power that comes from renewable resources: **11**

Percentage change, since 1980, in federal R&D spending on solar energy: **−90**

Percentage change, since 1980, in the cost of producing solar energy: **−73**

Chances that a piece of solar-energy equipment manufactured in the United States in 1989 was exported: **1 in 2**

Percentage change, from 1986 to 1990, in the number of yellow-pages listings for solar-energy equipment wholesalers: **−73**

Number of the solar panels installed on the White House roof by President Carter that are still there: **0**

Total area of solar panels required to fulfill all human energy needs, expressed as a percentage of the earth's landmass: **0.2**

Portion of the world's population that cooks with wood or charcoal: **1/2**

Portion of the world's oil production that is used for transportation in the United States: **1/6**

Estimated percentage of U.S. gasoline consumption that occurs during traffic jams: **4**

Average amount of gasoline President Bush's Cigarette boat consumes per hour, in gallons: **25**

Gas mileage of an M-1 tank, in miles per gallon: **0.56**

Change, since 1988, in the fuel efficiency of new automobiles sold in the United States, in miles per gallon: **−0.5**

Barrels of oil that could be saved by raising U.S. auto-efficiency standards by 2.75 miles per gallon: **290,000,000**

Barrels of oil the United States imported from Iraq and Kuwait in 1989: **290,000,000**

Amount of energy that leaks from windows in the United States each year, expressed in barrels of oil: **820,000,000**

Average portion of U.S. household electricity consumption that is used for cooling: **1/3**

Percentage of the solar energy captured on land by photosynthesis that is consumed by humans and livestock: **3**

Maximum voltage of an Amazonian electric eel: **650**

Watts of power used by the human brain when it is engaged in deep thought: **14**

Watts required to operate an IBM personal computer: **90**

Estimated amount of glucose used by an adult human brain each day, expressed in M&M's: **250**

Average number of calories burned by melting an ice cube in one's mouth: **2.3**

HEALTH RISKS

Number of U.S. factories that pose a "high risk" of cancer to nearby residents, according to the EPA: **149**

Chances that the blood of an American who uses a public water system contains a dangerous amount of lead: **1 in 5**

Percentage of the 164 local referendums proposing water fluoridation that have been voted down since 1980: **63**

Portion of American adults who don't drink: **1/3**

Rank of Nevada, the District of Columbia, and New Hampshire in per capita alcohol consumption: **1, 2, 3**

Chances that a Native American will die before the age of forty-five: **1 in 3**

Percentage increase, since 1979, in the number of deaths caused by asthma in the United States each year: **200**

Number of Americans who say they have quit smoking: **40,000,000**

Number who say they haven't quit smoking: **49,000,000**

Chances, in 1970, of an American woman developing breast cancer in her lifetime: **1 in 16**

Chances today: **1 in 10**

Percentage of Americans who say that a pregnant woman who smokes or drinks should be liable for harm to the fetus: **48**

Estimated number of women worldwide who die each year as a result of illegal abortions: **150,000**

Percentage of nursing mothers in North Carolina whose milk contains traces of PCBs: **87**

Percentage increase, since 1980, in cases of tuberculosis reported in New York City: **114**

Reported cases of rectal gonorrhea in San Francisco in 1980: **5,512**

Reported cases in 1989: **135**

Percentage decrease, since 1955, in the resident patient population of public U.S. psychiatric hospitals: **81**

Percentage decrease, since 1970, in the U.S. death rate due to strokes: **40**

Percentage decrease in the death rate due to heart disease: **14**

Minimum amount of saturated fat that Julia Child says she makes an effort to consume each day, in tablespoons: **2**

HEALTH CARE

Chances that an American under the age of sixty-five has no health insurance: **1 in 7**

Percentage of Medicare funds that go to people with less than a year to live: **28**

Total U.S. spending on health care in 1970, expressed as a percentage of the gross national product: **7.3**

Total U.S. spending on health care in 1989, expressed as a percentage of the gross national product: **11.6**

Percentage of total U.S. spending on health care in 1989 that was paid for by the government: **42**

Percentage of Americans who die in health-care institutions: **80**

Ratio of physicians to inhabitants in the United States: **1: 488**

Chances that a doctor practicing in the United States graduated from a foreign medical school: **1 in 6**

Percentage change, since 1979, in the number of white males applying to U.S. medical schools: **−47**

Chances, in 1982, that a resident in obstetrics and gynecology was a woman: **1 in 3**

Chances today: **1 in 2**

Chances that an American obstetrician has been sued for malpractice at least once: **7 in 10**

Chances that an obstetrician who is sued will win: **1 in 2**

Chances that a baby born in the United States in 1970 was delivered by cesarean section: **1 in 20**

WHAT COUNTS

Chances that a baby born today is: **1 in 4**

Percentage of U.S. counties in which there are no doctors' offices, clinics, or hospitals that perform abortions: **82**

Percentage of pregnant American women who receive no prenatal care during the first three months of pregnancy: **24**

Percentage of Medicaid-application rejections that are the result of problems with paperwork or documentation: **60**

Portion of hospital beds in American cities in 1950 that were in public hospitals: **1/3**

Portion that are in public hospitals today: **1/7**

Membership of Physicians for Social Responsibility in 1980: **800**

Membership in 1990: **27,126**

Number of medical doctors who belong to the Surfer's Medical Association, worldwide: **700**

Percentage of doctors who smoke: **17**

Percentage of visits to doctors' offices that last less than eleven minutes: **41**

Chances that a doctor is a union member: **1 in 10**

Average number of U.S. doctors whose licenses are revoked each year: **440**

Percentage of Americans who say that doctors in hospitals should wear white coats: **65**

Chances that a pharmaceutical is derived from a plant: **1 in 4**

Number of leeches sold each year to American surgeons and hospitals by Leeches USA of Westbury, New York: **10,000**

Estimated average distance that a New York City hospital nurse walks on the job each year, in miles: **1,272**

Estimated average distance that a New York City dentist walks, in miles: **204**

Percentage of all dental patients who say they like dentists to wear protective gloves "because of the taste": **1**

THE AIDS VIRUS

Estimated number of AIDS cases in 1990, worldwide: **1,000,000**

Estimated number of years it will take for the number of AIDS cases, worldwide, to double: **3**

Portion of all U.S. AIDS deaths since 1981 that took place in 1990: **1/3**

Percentage of Americans who say they run no risk of getting AIDS: **78**

Percentage of Americans who believe that AIDS is "a pun-

ishment God has given homosexuals for the way they live":
27

Estimated percentage of all AIDS cases, worldwide, that were caused by heterosexual contact: **60**

Number of Americans who had died of AIDS before President Reagan first discussed the issue in a speech: **21,000**

Average number of hours of nursing care a hospitalized AIDS patient requires each day: **9**

Average number of hours of nursing care a hospitalized AIDS patient receives each day: **4.5**

Estimated amount Americans spend on bogus AIDS treatment each year: **$1,000,000,000**

Rank of AIDS, among the leading causes of death of children between the ages of one and four in New York City: **1**

Rank of AIDS, among the leading causes of death for women between the ages of twenty-five and thirty-nine in New York City: **1**

Chances that a New York City prison inmate will test positive for the AIDS virus: **1 in 5**

Percentage change in the price of blood in New York City since 1980: **+107**

Percentage of Americans who say they have little or no sympathy for "people who get AIDS from homosexual activity": **60**

Percentage of Americans who believe that "some civil liberties must be suspended in the war on AIDS": **43**

Number of the 122,000 Illinois marriage-license applicants screened for AIDS in 1989 who tested positive: **26**

PSYCHOLOGY

Anxiety
Narcissism
Fears
Beliefs

ANXIETY

Number of mental disorders recognized by the American Psychiatric Association in 1952: **110**

Number recognized today: **220**

Amount the New York City Transit Authority spent in 1990 on psychological counseling for its executives: **$11,500**

Estimated number of state and local government antinoise programs in 1978: **1,100**

Estimated number today: **15**

Chances that an American "always feels rushed": **1 in 3**

Ratio of the number of men who are chronically constipated to the number of women who are: **2:1**

Average duration of an adult's cry, in minutes: **6**

Percentage of Fortune 500 executives who say they "lose sleep" over the competition: **14**

Percentage of thirteen- to fifteen-year-old American boys who say "thinking or talking about sex scares me": **16**

Portion of fourth graders who say that there is peer pressure to try wine coolers: **1/3**

Percentage of the applicants for the 1990 kindergarten class at Manhattan's Trinity School who were rejected: **80**

Percentage of applicants for the 1990 freshman class at Stanford University who were: **78**

Percentage of American college students who say that they spend more than half their waking hours worrying: **15**

Percentage of sixteen- to nineteen-year-old Japanese teenagers who say that they "worry very much about almost everything": **73**

NARCISSISM

Percentage of Americans who say that, even if they could, they would not change anything about their appearance: **4**

Number of cosmetic surgical procedures performed on Americans in 1988: **619,565**

Pounds of fat that cosmetic surgeons remove from Americans each year: **200,000**

Pounds of silicone and collagen implanted in Americans each year: **60,000**

Average bra size worn by an American woman in 1985: **34B**

Average size today: **36C**

Price of a pair of pectoral implants for men, from Dr. Brian Novack of Beverly Hills, California: **$6,500**

Price of a full back-waxing for men at La Carezza in New York City: **$30**

Estimated speed of human hair growth, in miles per hour: **0.00000001**

Change, since 1988, in the average number of minutes an American man spends on personal grooming each day: **+15**

Percentage of men who say that "foot odor is a concern": **54**

Number of the 43 contestants in the 1990 Odor-Eaters Rotten Sneaker Contest who were women: **1**

Percentage of American men who admit they wear uncomfortable shoes because they look good: **20**

Percentage of American women who admit this: **45**

Average percentage increase in the protrusion of a woman's buttocks when she wears high heels: **25**

Average weight of a female fashion model in 1970, in pounds: **112**

Average weight in 1990, in pounds: **130**

Estimated percentage of American adults who go on a diet each year: **44**

Average number of pounds that American men add to their weight when reporting it: **0.91**

Average number of pounds that American women subtract: **2.3**

WHAT COUNTS

Barbie's measurements (if she were life-size): **39-23-33**

Percentage of American women who consider themselves pretty: **13**

Percentage of American men who consider themselves handsome: **28**

Average number of sex-change operations performed in the United States each year: **225**

Price of a thirty-minute collagen injection procedure to fatten lips: **$750**

Percentage of Americans who think they look younger than they are: **57**

Percentage of Iowans who would like to be reincarnated as themselves: **64**

Percentage of Americans who say they have a good sense of humor: **85**

Average score Americans give themselves on a 1-to-10 scale of looks: **6.5**

Acres of mirrors in Donald Trump's Taj Mahal casino in Atlantic City: **10**

Average number of moles on an adult's body: **25**

Percentage change, since 1988, in the number of yellow-pages listings for tanning salons: **+17**

Percentage of women's bathing suits sold in 1977 that were bikinis: **51**

Percentage of those sold in 1990 that were: **12**

Estimated amount Princess Diana has spent on underwear since marrying Prince Charles: **$26,460**

Average number of days a West German man goes without changing his underwear: **7**

Amount the Reverend Al Sharpton spends each year on hair care at the PrimaDonna beauty salon in Brooklyn: **$2,000**

Melting point of Dippity-do: **122°F**

FEARS

Average age at which an American develops a phobia: **13.5**

Rank of being home alone, among children's most common fears: **1**

Rank of kidnapping, drugs, and car accidents, among the dangers to children most feared by parents: **1, 2, 3**

Percentage of scientists who say they would permit their child to have contact with a schoolmate with AIDS: **39**

Number of condoms the rock group Poison brought on their 1988 tour: **876**

Number of Band-Aids: **2,482**

Number of Geiger counters Christie Brinkley carried with her on a 1988 trip to the Soviet Union: **1**

Percentage of Americans who say that Soviet nuclear weapons are a "very serious" threat to national security: **43**

Percentage who say that environmental problems are: **74**

Number of calls made each day to the hot line for the Society for Secular Armageddonism, in San Francisco: **50**

Percentage change in sales of the predictions of Nostradamus at Waldenbooks in the month after the Iraqi invasion of Kuwait: **+400**

Amount the U.S. government spent in 1990 on lead-lined trucks to house the administration during a nuclear attack: **$57,990,000**

Price of a fully equipped 1990 Cadillac that can "withstand heavy artillery," from The Spy Connection in Hawthorne, California: **$111,000**

Price of a bullet-resistant mink coat from Zizzo Bullet Proof Fashions in New York City: **$15,000**

Percentage of white Americans who believe their homes are secure from crime: **75**

Percentage of black Americans who believe their homes are secure: **57**

Amount spent in the United States in 1990 on private security forces: **$52,000,000,000**

Estimated number of times Salman Rushdie moved during the six months after his death threat was issued: **56**

Rank of being at a party with strangers, among situations that make adults anxious: **1**

PSYCHOLOGY

Percentage of Americans who say they would rather have a tooth pulled than take a car in for repairs: **20**

Rank of "crashing and dying," among the reasons people say they most fear flying: **4**

Chances that a California homeowner has earthquake insurance: **1 in 6**

Ratio of Americans killed by lightning each year to Americans killed by fireworks: **15:1**

Percentage of Americans who say that mowing the lawn is "risky": **54**

Average number of Americans who are injured by chain saws each year: **36,000**

Average number who are injured by clothing: **112,000**

BELIEFS

Percentage of Americans who say that God has spoken to them: **36**

Percentage of Americans who regularly attend religious services: **43**

Rank of Mass, bingo, and religious education, among the most popular activities at U.S. Catholic churches: **1, 2, 3**

Percentage of Americans who say that some numbers are especially lucky for some people: **39**

Percentage of Americans who believe in miracles: **80**

Number of Americans currently being considered by the Vatican for sainthood: **29**

Estimated chances that a Catholic priest in the United States is sexually active: **1 in 2**

Percentage of abortions in the United States that are performed on Catholic women: **32**

Percentage change, since 1975, in church attendance by American Catholics: **−7.5**

Percentage change, since 1975, in church attendance by American Protestants: **+5.2**

Percentage change, since 1976, in membership in the Mormon Church: **+95**

Chances that a resident of Santa Fe is a "healer" of some kind: **1 in 52**

Percentage of Americans who believe in reincarnation: **23**

Average number of Russian Orthodox churches reopened in the Soviet Union each week in 1989: **56**

Number of tourists in Jerusalem, since 1988, who have received psychiatric treatment for religious delusions: **152**

Endowment of the Jackie Mason Lectureship in Contemporary Judaism at Oxford University, in pounds: **125,000**

Average number of Latin American Catholics who convert to evangelical Christianity each hour: **400**

Number of priests and nuns expelled from Chile since 1973: **138**

Suggested donation for a Latin Mass on videocassette from the Catholic Traditionalist Movement in Westbury, Connecticut: **$40**

Number of Christian music videos sold in 1989: **6,000,000**

Percentage of Americans who watch an evangelical religious program on television at least once a week: **28**

Rank of Washington, D.C., among U.S. cities with the highest per capita viewership of television evangelists: **1**

Number of evangelical broadcast ministries that are currently being investigated by the IRS: **22**

Average number of minutes Jerry Falwell spent soliciting contributions during each "Old Time Gospel Hour": **26**

Percentage of Americans who say that they have communicated with the devil: **10**

Number of women appointed Official Salem Witch by Governor Michael Dukakis: **1**

Number of astrologers in the United States: **7,500**

Number of astronomers: **4,960**

Percentage of Americans who expect to go to heaven: **66**

WHAT COUNTS

Members of the Christian Motorcyclists Association: **33,805**

Cost of having a car blessed at the Daishi Buddhist temple in Kawasaki, Japan: **$22.65**

Number of pets blessed at the Feast of St. Francis of Assisi at New York's Cathedral of St. John the Divine in 1989: **1,000**

Number of bowls of algae blessed: **1**

HOME EC

▪▪▪▪▪▪▪▪▪▪▪▪▪▪▪▪▪▪▪▪▪▪▪▪▪▪▪▪▪

Married Life

Modern Baby Making

Family Affairs

Around the House

Edibles and Potables

Shelter

Pets

MARRIED LIFE

Chances that an American wedding will occur in June: **1 in 9**

Rank of January, among months in which the fewest weddings take place: **1**

Percentage of married Americans who say they were worried about sex on their wedding night: **19**

Percentage who say they were worried about finances: **67**

Average cost of a wedding, expressed as a portion of the median annual income of a family of four: **2/5**

Tons of gold made into wedding rings each year in the United States: **17**

Chances that a bride or fiancée whose picture appeared in the Sunday *New York Times* in June 1990 wore pearls: **3 in 5**

Government-approved dowry for a bride in Rwanda, in garden hoes: **3**

Number of guests at the wedding of Ronald Reagan's daughter Patti in 1984: **134**

Number of police officers and Secret Service agents: **180**

Price of a wedding ceremony at the coin-operated, twenty-four-hour Church of Elvis in Portland, Oregon: **$1**

Estimated chances that an American couple married this year will get divorced: **3 in 5**

Average duration of an American marriage before divorce, in years: **9.6**

Chances that a white, college-educated, single twenty-five-year-old woman will marry: **1 in 2**

Chances that a white, college-educated, single, thirty-five-year-old woman will: **1 in 18**

Percentage of cohabiting couples who were unwed in 1970: **1**

Percentage who were in 1988: **5**

Percentage of West Germans who say that good sex is "very important" to a marriage: **52**

Percentage of Americans who say this: **75**

Percentage of American married couples who say they never take baths or showers together: **37**

Average number of years of marriage before an unfaithful British husband has his first affair: **8**

Average number of years before an unfaithful British wife does: **9**

Number of gay marriages that have taken place in Denmark since they became legally binding there in 1989: **671**

Chances that a Swedish couple who married without first living together will eventually separate: **1 in 4**

Chances that a Swedish couple who married after first living together will separate: **1 in 3**

Percentage of American men who say they would marry the same woman if they had it to do all over again: **80**

Percentage of women who say they would marry the same man: **50**

Ratio of the number of divorce suits filed by women to the number filed by men: **2:1**

Average number of days a divorced middle-aged woman spends sick in bed each year: **14**

Average number of days a married middle-aged woman spends sick in bed each year: **7**

Percentage of men who say they are happier since their divorce or separation: **58**

Percentage of women who say this: **85**

Percentage of married women in the United States who say they have been raped by their husbands: **14**

Number of states in which marital rape is not a crime: **8**

Chances that a woman abused by her husband who does not notify the police will be assaulted again within the next six months: **2 in 5**

Average number of wives burned to death by their husbands each day in India: **5**

Weight of a Bridgeport, Connecticut, woman who killed her husband in 1989 by sitting on him, in pounds: **475**

MODERN BABY MAKING

Number of Americans who were conceived in a test tube: **5,500**

Estimated number of Americans carried to term by surrogate mothers: **4,000**

Average fee charged by a surrogate mother: **$10,000**

Number of babies conceived in the United States in 1988 with sperm from an anonymous donor: **30,000**

Percentage of doctors who say they would allow a woman to choose a sperm donor based on his religion: **56**

Percentage of doctors who say they would reject an unmarried woman's request for artificial insemination: **50**

Chances that an American woman will become pregnant by the age of twenty: **2 in 5**

Chances that an American woman will have an abortion in her lifetime: **1 in 2**

Percentage of Americans who say that parents should not be allowed to choose the sex of their child: **69**

Chances that a child born to a married couple was accidentally conceived: **1 in 10**

Chances that a child born out of wedlock was accidentally conceived: **1 in 4**

Percentage of children born in 1960 who were firstborns: **26**

Percentage of children born in 1987 who were: **41**

Number of abortions for every 100 pregnancies in the United States: **25**

Ratio of the number of babies born to the number of televisions produced each year in the United States: **1:3**

Rank of Utah, Arizona, and Alaska among states with the highest birthrate: **1, 2, 3**

Estimated decrease in the number of U.S. births in the spring if the previous summer's temperature is five degrees above normal: **10,000**

Rank of the summer, among seasons in which the greatest number of Americans are born: **1**

Estimated percentage of boys born in the United States in 1989 who were circumcised: **60**

Percentage of boys born in Britain in 1989 who were: **0.4**

Price of a baby-nursing "Baby Bonder Vest" for fathers, bottle not included: **$24.95**

Chances that a woman will return to work within twelve months of giving birth: **1 in 2**

Estimated number of disposable diapers discarded each year by Americans: **17,000,000,000**

Cost of tuition for two parents at Philadelphia's Better Baby Institute: **$1,380**

Price of *Video Baby*, a tape offering "the experience of having a baby without the mess and inconvenience of the real thing": **$14.95**

FAMILY AFFAIRS

Percentage change, since 1980, in the number of American families made up of a housewife, an employed husband, and two children: **−21**

Portion of American families headed by a single parent: **1/4**

Percentage of American households that consist of a father and children he is raising alone: **1.6**

Percentage of fathers who win the child-custody cases they contest: **70**

Estimated percentage of missing American children who have been abducted by strangers: **0.33**

Percentage of adults who say they were first told the facts of life by their mothers: **17**

Percentage who say they were first told the facts of life by their fathers: **2**

Percentage of American fathers who say that they should share child care equally with their wives: **74**

Percentage who say they do share child care equally with their wives: **13**

Percentage of fourth graders who say that their parents never read to them: **13**

Percentage of American parents who say that they yell at their children every day: **19**

Average number of seconds each day that a working couple spend in "meaningful conversation" with their children: **30**

Percentage increase, since 1965, in the number of young married couples with children: **7**

Percentage increase in the number without children: **80**

Chances that an American household was comprised of a single person in 1955: **1 in 10**

Chances in 1989: **1 in 4**

Percentage of American children who live with two parents: **72**

Percentage of American parents who say they spank their children: **83**

Percentage of these parents who say they consider spanking seldom, if ever, effective: **40**

Percentage of Pittsburghers who named family members when asked which household pests they fear most: **1.3**

Percentage of Americans between the ages of eight and seventeen who say they have five or more living grandparents: **8**

Percentage of American parents over the age of sixty-five who talk to their children on the telephone each day: **42**

Percentage of Americans over the age of sixty-five who live with a younger relative: **6**

Number of different familial relationships for which Hallmark makes cards: **105**

AROUND THE HOUSE

Average number of times an American opens the refrigerator each day: **22**

Percentage of refrigerators in American households that are either white or almond: **99**

Portion of all U.S. telephones that are in the kitchen: **1/3**

Chances that an American will use a recipe when cooking dinner: **1 in 5**

Percentage of Americans who say that the leftovers in their refrigerator are more than four weeks old: **5**

Estimated amount Americans spend each year to kill household roaches: **$124,000,000**

Percentage of Americans who eat dinner between 5:00 P.M. and 8:00 P.M.: **90**

Percentage of men in two-income families who say they "almost always" wash the dishes: **6**

Percentage of women in two-income families who say they "almost always" prepare the tax returns: **29**

Average cost of planting a ten-by-twenty-foot vegetable garden: **$36**

Average value of a garden's yield of vegetables: **$175**

Estimated number of acres of residential lawn in the United States: **7,650,000**

Percentage of American households that own three or more cars: **11**

Chances that an American commuter eats breakfast in his or her car: **1 in 4**

Chances that an American will skip breakfast: **1 in 10**

Percentage of Americans who say they are at their best in the morning: **56**

Percentage who say they are at their best after midnight: **2**

Percentage of men between the ages of forty and sixty-four who snore heavily: **60**

Number of bedrooms in the United States: **260,387,000**

Percentage of American men who say they sleep in the nude: **26**

Percentage of women who say they do: **6**

Average amount of laundry an American family of four washes in a year, in tons: **1**

Percentage of families in Iowa in which the wife does the laundry: **87**

Percentage in which the husband takes out the trash: **55**

Maximum annual earnings allowed entrants in the Eagle Forum Homemaker of the Year contest: **$500**

Price of CyberVac, a self-navigating robotic vacuum cleaner, from Cyberworks of Ontario, Canada: **$10,500**

Percentage of American households whose TV sets have remote control: **79**

Number of emergency-room visits resulting from bathtub or shower injuries in 1989: **117,283**

Average number of bunk-bed-related injuries each year in the United States: **28,500**

Percentage of American parents who say that their grown child's old bedroom has been "preserved as a shrine": **4**

EDIBLES AND POTABLES

Chances that an American has had a pizza delivered in the last three months: **1 in 2**

Average number of pounds of pasta an American eats each year: **16**

Average number of pounds an Italian eats: **55**

Percentage increase, since 1984, in the number of vegetarians in England: **76**

Rank of the United States, Singapore, and Israel in per capita consumption of poultry: **1, 2, 3**

Average number of pigs an American eats in a lifetime: **28**

Portion of the U.S. luncheon-meat market controlled by Spam: **3/4**

Average amount of food an American consumes each year, in pounds: **1,400**

Average number of apples an American ate in 1910: **135**

Average number an American eats today: **48**

Average amount an American household spends on vegetables each week: **$2.13**

Percentage change, since 1971, in per capita consumption of fresh broccoli: **+557**

Maximum number of aphids that FDA regulations permit in a pound of frozen broccoli: **272**

Rank of China, among all countries, in annual cauliflower production: **1**

Rank of the Soviet Union, among all countries, in annual cabbage production: **1**

WHAT COUNTS

Liters of vodka drunk in the Soviet Union in 1984: **2,577,000,000**

Liters drunk in 1990: **1,600,000,000**

Tons of shaved ice needed each year to make mint juleps for the Kentucky Derby: **60**

Percentage of the tea drunk by Americans that is iced: **80**

Average number of cups of coffee an American drinks each day: **3.4**

Number of Americans who consume at least ten cups of coffee each day: **385,000**

Rank of Miami, among all cities, in prune juice consumption per household: **1**

Rank of tofu, liver, and yogurt, among foods that Americans hate most: **1, 2, 3**

Price of an order of sushi at Dodger Stadium during the 1988 season: **$4.50**

Pounds of fish consumed each day at Le Bernardin restaurant in New York City: **400**

Pounds of fish consumed each day at the Monterey Bay Aquarium in California: **125**

Estimated amount that Bryan Miller, the *New York Times* food critic, spends on restaurant meals each year: **$80,000**

Chances that a restaurant bill is incorrect: **1 in 8**

Percentage of Americans who have tried caviar and say they "really liked" it: **8**

HOME EC

Average number of frogs eaten by the French each year: **200,000,000**

Tons of smoked salmon eaten at Wimbledon in 1990: **18**

Tons of strawberries eaten: **23**

Percentage of Kellogg's Frosted Flakes eaters who are adults: **50**

Rank of Portland, Oregon, among all U.S. cities, in per capita consumption of Grape-Nuts: **1**

Grams of saturated fat in three ounces of Nature Valley Fruit and Nuts Granola: **13.3**

Grams of saturated fat in three ounces of Ben & Jerry's vanilla ice cream: **7.5**

Change, since 1986, in the number of Americans who say they are on a diet: **– 17,000,000**

Number of the 12,055 supermarket products introduced in 1989 that were condiments: **1,701**

Percentage change, since 1981, in per capita U.S. consumption of white bread: **– 5**

Chances that an American has never bought a bagel: **2 in 3**

Paces at which the crunch of a pickle should be audible, according to Pickle Packers International: **10**

SHELTER

Increase, since 1980, in the median cost of a new home, in constant dollars: **$16,170**

Increase, since 1980, in the median income of an American, in constant dollars: **$64**

Estimated number of vacant New York City apartments that landlords kept off the market in 1990: **70,000**

Estimated number of New York City residents temporarily living with others because they have no apartment: **460,000**

Combined value of the mortgages given by East Harlem bank branches to local residents in 1989, expressed as a percentage of deposits: **1**

Average number of homeless people in New York City shelters and welfare hotels each day in 1990: **20,500**

Number of shelters for battered women in the United States in 1970: **0**

Number of shelters for battered women today: **1,500**

Number of years the average homeless person lives on the street: **7**

Percentage change, since 1981, in federal funds for subsidized housing: **−72**

HOME EC

Amount spent on federal housing programs in 1990: **$15,400,000,000**

Federal tax revenues lost as a result of homeowners' mortgage interest deductions in 1990: **$54,700,000,000**

Estimated waiting time for a vacancy in a New York City public housing project, in years: **3**

Total contributions by individuals in 1989 to New York City's Coalition for the Homeless: **$622,000**

Total contribution by individuals in 1989 to New York City's Bide-a-Wee Home Association for pets: **$1,700,000**

Federal housing funds spent by New Jersey's Passaic Housing Authority in 1988 and 1989 to feed stray cats: **$14,865**

Number of bat houses sold since 1986 by Bat Conservation International of Austin, Texas: **9,174**

Estimated number of Egyptians who are living in Cairo's cemeteries and tombs: **14,000**

Number of Palestinian homes in the West Bank and Gaza Strip that have been demolished or sealed by Israel since 1967: **1,700**

Ratio of real-estate agents to residents in Greenwich, Connecticut: **1:83**

Average percentage of annual income that a homeowner spent on mortgage payments in 1970: **17**

Average percentage today: **22**

Average number of homes an American lives in during his or her lifetime: **30**

Number of households that have been relocated since 1982 because of toxic dumping: **1,538**

Estimated number of families who have applied to purchase homes at Love Canal since they were offered for sale in 1990: **335**

Percentage of thirty- to thirty-four-year-old heads of households in 1975 who owned their own homes: **62**

Percentage in 1990 who did: **52**

Average number of homes a buyer looks at before making a purchase: **14**

Price of a night's stay in an underwater room at Jules's Undersea Lodge in Key Largo, Florida (including food and air): **$195**

Price of a night in the Alexander the Great Suite of Donald Trump's Taj Mahal casino, per minute: **$7**

Amount the town of Rolfe, Iowa, will pay anyone who builds a home there: **$1,200**

PETS

Ratio of American children to American cats and dogs: **1:2**

Cost of raising a medium-size dog to the age of eleven: **$6,400**

Price of a twenty-five-ounce bottle of Mon Chien, "a ground-beef flavored alternative to water" for dogs: **$9.72**

Estimated number of pounces it takes a cat to catch a mouse: **3**

Chances that a cat will die after a fall from six stories: **1 in 10**

Chances that a person will die after a fall from six stories: **9 in 10**

Number of Americans killed by pit bulls since 1986: **35**

Percentage of veterinarians who say that they have felt depressed after putting an animal to sleep: **67**

Number of people who attended the funeral in 1989 of Reveille IV, a collie that was the mascot of Texas A&M: **10,000**

Price of Pet Rest, which includes "a casket, white satin liner, name tag, and sympathy card," for a guinea pig: **$14.99**

Number of pet cemeteries in the United States: **450**

Number of pet-death support groups in the United States: **65**

Percentage of dogs that are overweight: **40**

Shelf space taken up by canned pet food in the average American supermarket, in feet: **163**

Shelf space taken up by canned soup, in feet: **104**

Estimated number of American dogs that have been named as beneficiaries in a will: **1,000,000**

Percentage of pet owners who keep a photograph of their pet in their wallet: **40**

Price of dyeing a dog pink at the Village Dawg Shoppe in

WHAT COUNTS

Rockville Centre, New York (with shampoo and cut): **$87**

Price of a purple mohawk: **$47**

Price of *Video Dog*, a tape offering the "experience of owning a pet without the mess and inconvenience of the real thing": **$14.95**

Number of calls received by the Illinois Animal Poison Information Center in 1989 regarding pets that had swallowed marijuana: **68**

Average number of parrots smuggled into the United States from Mexico each day: **274**

Number of subscribers to the *Ostrich News*, worldwide: **2,300**

Percentage of tropical-fish owners in Iowa who say they wish their pets were more affectionate: **40**

VACATION

~~~~~~~~~~~~~~~~~~

Holidays

Travel and Tourism

The Sporting Life

The Great Outdoors

Leisure Time

Junk Food

Sex

HOLIDAYS

Average number of Christmas cards received by an American household each year: **26**

Ratio of the number of U.S. households that have real Christmas trees to those that have artificial ones: **1:1**

Percentage of Jewish households in the United States that have Christmas trees: **16**

Number of U.S. cities and towns named Santa Claus: **3**

Percentage of child psychologists who advise parents of pre-school children to "confirm Santa's existence": **40**

Number of records, cassettes, and compact discs of "White Christmas" that have been sold in North America since its release: **214,067,641**

Portion of the New York City Ballet's ticket income derived from performances of *The Nutcracker*: **1/4**

Price of a pound of reindeer meat at Lobel's Prime Meats in New York City: **$19.98**

Estimated cost of a partridge in a pear tree, retail: **$39.95**

Of three French hens: **$15**

Of seven swans a-swimming: **$7,000**

Percentage of Americans who say they ate plum pudding last Christmas: **1**

Estimated total value of the candy purchased each Halloween: **$1,000,000,000**

Number of Valentine's Day cards purchased in 1989: **900,000,000**

Percentage of these that were sent by women: **85**

Ratio of the number of women who buy Father's Day cards to the number of men who do: **8:1**

Ratio of the number of women who buy Mother's Day cards to the number of men who do: **5:1**

Rank of Mother's Day, among holidays, in the number of long-distance phone calls placed in 1989: **1**

Rank of Mother's Day, among holidays, in the number of Americans who eat out: **1**

Average number of calories an American consumes during Thanksgiving dinner: **1,960**

Estimated number of calories a Thanksgiving turkey consumes in its lifetime: **100,000**

World's record for the largest turkey ever raised, in pounds: **75**

Rank of the holiday season, among the busiest times of the year for plastic surgeons: **1**

TRAVEL AND TOURISM

Number of Americans holding reservations with Pan Am for a trip to the moon: **30,000**

Portion of the American population that has never flown in an airplane: **1/5**

Total number of frequent-flier miles U.S. airlines owe their passengers: **870,000,000,000**

Total distance of a round-trip to Pluto, in miles: **7,000,000,000**

Price of renting the *Queen Elizabeth II* for an overnight "cruise to nowhere" for six hundred guests: **$500,000**

Price of a fourteen-day ski trip to Antarctica, from Adventure Network: **$7,990**

Ratio of the number of tourists to the number of scientists and researchers visiting Antarctica each year: **1:1**

Estimated number of people per square mile during peak season in the Yosemite Valley: **3,320**

Number of people per square mile in Houston: **2,986**

Number of the 989 people who have died in U.S. national parks since 1983 who were killed by animals: **3**

WHAT COUNTS

Average number of people airborne over the United States each hour: **61,000**

Percentage of Americans who have visited Disneyland or Disney World: **70**

Percentage who have visited Washington, D.C.: **60**

Percentage of Iowans who say they would rather spend a weekend in Des Moines than in San Francisco: **31**

THE SPORTING LIFE

Ratio of U.S. annual spending on baseball cards to spending on tickets to major-league games: **5:1**

Number of season tickets to spring training sold by the Los Angeles Dodgers in 1990: **3,269**

Number sold in 1977: **630**

Percentage of baseball players signed to professional contracts who never appear in a major-league game: **90**

Number of newspaper and magazine articles about baseball contracts and salaries published since 1980: **2,459**

Number of articles about drug abuse in baseball published since 1980: **6,071**

Percentage by which the sales of the *Sports Illustrated* swimsuit issue exceed sales of the average issue: **50**

Estimated amount of time that Michael Jordan has spent aloft during his NBA career, in hours: **3**

Estimated number of college basketball coaches who are on the payroll of sneaker companies: **100**

Average increase in an NBA team's season attendance when a black player is replaced by a comparable white: **10,000**

Amount by which the height of basketball player Manute Bol exceeds the diameter of the Wheel of Fortune, in inches: **1**

Number of weeks after Ken Griffey, Jr., began playing major-league baseball that the Ken Griffey, Jr., candy bar went on the market: **5**

Price paid at auction in 1991 for a 1909 Honus Wagner baseball card: **$451,000**

Number of professional baseballs produced each year in Haiti, per Haitian: **1**

Number of minutes it takes to hand-stitch a baseball: **11**

Estimated number of ash trees used to supply major-league baseball teams with Louisville Sluggers in 1990: **4,800**

Number of baseball gloves that can be made from one cow: **5**

Pounds of mud for rubbing baseballs bought by major-league teams each year from Burns Bintliff of Millsboro, Delaware: **182**

Life span of a baseball in a major-league game, in pitches: **7**

Portion by which a baseball is compressed when hit squarely: **1/4**

Number of the 206 players in baseball's Hall of Fame who wore glasses while on the field: **4**

Number of former major-league baseball players whose fathers are in the Hall of Fame: **9**

Number of former major-league players whose last names are palindromes: **7**

Percentage of Americans who believe their presence at a sports event influences its outcome: **25**

Average electric bill for a night game at New York City's Shea Stadium: **$4,000**

Total horsepower at the 1990 Indianapolis 500: **24,000**

Total horsepower at the 1990 Kentucky Derby: **750**

Maximum speed of a hockey puck in an NHL game, in miles per hour: **96**

Average speed of the winner in the men's five-thousand-meter race at the 1912 Olympics, in miles per hour: **12.8**

Average speed of the winner at the 1988 Olympics, in miles per hour: **14.1**

World's record for underwater pogo-sticking in the Amazon, in hours: **3.66**

Winning time in the 1990 International Window Cleaners Association Squeegee Speed Competition, in seconds: **10.48**

THE GREAT OUTDOORS

Average percentage of his or her lifetime that an American spends outdoors: **3**

Percentage of Americans who own running shoes but don't run: **87**

Estimated amount of body fluids lost through perspiration per hour of exercise in hot weather, in ounces: **54**

Estimated number of base-sliding injuries that occur in softball games each year: **1,700,000**

Number of croquet clubs in the United States in 1977: **5**

Number in 1990: **320**

Percentage change, since 1977, in sales of tennis rackets: **−137**

Number of cheerleaders in the United States: **750,000**

Number of rescues made by lifeguards on Southern California beaches in 1989: **35,841**

Number of Americans killed by sharks since 1988: **6**

Price of a thirty-minute swim with dolphins at Dolphins Plus in Key Largo: **$60**

Percentage of registered Democrats who say their favorite spectator sport is fishing: **2**

Percentage of liberals who say they've gone skinny-dipping: **28**

Percentage of conservatives who say they have: **15**

Estimated percentage increase in sales of horseshoes since George Bush took office: **20**

Average number of golf games Dan Quayle played each week in 1987, while he was a senator: **3**

Rounds of golf played in America each year: **474,000,000**

Average number of holes in one that American golfers claim to hit each day: **95**

Amount Americans bet on greyhounds each year: **$3,000,000,000**

Number of states in which cockfighting is legal: **4**

Amount the U.S. Army spent in 1990 on recreational target-practice programs for civilians: **$5,000,000**

Attendance at a "reenactment" of the U.S. invasion of Panama, held at McChord Air Force Base in Tacoma, Washington, in July 1990: **125,000**

Entry fee for the Defense Research Institute's 1988 Benefit Dove Shoot in Hope Hull, Alabama: **$250**

Estimated percentage of Georgia hunting injuries that result from hunters falling out of trees: **36**

Chances that an animal caught in a trap is discarded because it is not the targeted animal: **1 in 4**

Amount paid at auction for a hunting permit to kill one big-horn sheep in Montana in 1990: **$61,000**

Maximum number of fish a person may shoot each day in Lake Champlain, Vermont: **10**

Number of Wisconsin's 33 state senators who voted in favor of a 1988 bill that allows the blind to hunt: **27**

LEISURE TIME

Rank of TV viewing, eating, and shopping, among activities Americans spend the most leisure time engaged in: **1, 2, 3**

Number of uninterrupted hours that a Boston girl played Nintendo before having an epileptic seizure in 1990: **3**

Price of Homework First, a Nintendo video-game lock: **$9.95**

Average annual percentage increase in U.S. video-game sales since 1985: **120**

Estimated number of frames bowled in U.S. ten-pin alleys each year: **7,700,000,000**

Possible games of chess: 25×10^{120}

Rank of the longest paper-clip, gum-wrapper, or rubber-band

chain, among the entries most often rejected by the *Guinness Book of World Records*: **1**

Acres of crossword puzzles Americans fill in each day: **54**

Number of butterfly parks in the United States: **3**

Price of a week's stay for a family of four at the Solair Nudist Park in Massachusetts: **$260**

Estimated number of gallons of suntan lotion and oil bought by Americans in 1989: **1,500,000**

Number of backyard swimming pools in the United States in 1977: **1,330,000**

Number in 1990: **6,000,000**

Average number of hours an American spends mowing the lawn each year: **30**

Estimated number of charcoal briquettes sold in 1989: **17,850,000,000**

Percentage of American barbecuers who combine microwave cooking with outdoor grilling: **53**

Average number of laughs a person has in a day: **17**

Average number of dreams an adult has in a year: **1,600**

Average number of nightmares: **1.5**

Chances that an American adult will report having had a "great" night last night: **1 in 7**

JUNK FOOD

Estimated number of M&M's sold each day in the United States: **200,000,000**

Estimated number of unfilled cavities in the United States: **500,000,000**

Pounds of free Doritos distributed in Daytona Beach, Florida, during the 1989 spring break: **1,982**

Ratio of the amount Americans spent in 1989 on candy to the amount they spent on cookies: **2:1**

Packets of Kool-Aid sent to American soldiers in the Persian Gulf in 1990 by a Pennsylvania chapter of the Veterans of Foreign Wars: **3,040**

Percentage of Americans who drink soft drinks in the morning: **10**

Average number of Coca-Cola commercials an American sees each year: **75**

Amount of time it would take for all the Coca-Cola ever sold to flow over Niagara Falls, in hours: **23**

Number of Twinkies that Twinkie inventor Jimmy Dewar ate in his lifetime: **40,177**

Portion of the ice cream sold in the United States in 1976 that was vanilla: **1/2**

Portion sold in 1989 that was: **1/3**

Percentage of American consumers of low-calorie or diet foods who say they are not on a diet: **59**

Chances that an American adult is obese: **1 in 4**

Ounces of Coke called for in the recipe for Fruited Pork Chops in *Cooking with Coca-Cola*, a pamphlet distributed by the Coca-Cola Company: **4**

Percentage increase, since 1980, in the U.S. consumption of potato chips: **71**

Rank of the Navajo tribe, among the largest supplier of potatoes to Frito-Lay: **1**

Portion of the U.S. potato crop that is french fried: **1/3**

Percentage of Americans who know what a Whopper is: **95**

Percentage of Americans who eat at McDonald's each day: **7**

Number of months the managers of the Moscow McDonald's attended the Canadian Institute of Hamburgerology in 1989: **9**

Percentage of fast-food workers who say they are satisfied with their jobs: **61**

Acres of pizza consumed each day in the United States: **90**

Number of times a nude or seminude woman accepted a Domino's Pizza delivery in Washington, D.C., in 1990: **15**

VACATION

Number of deaths in 1988 caused by accidents involving Domino's Pizza delivery trucks: **20**

Number of deaths in 1989 caused by vending machines falling on people who shook them: **2**

SEX

Percentage of American men who say they enjoy sex more than money: **47**

Percentage of American women who say they enjoy sex more than money: **26**

Percentage of American women who say they enjoy neither sex nor money: **16**

Chances that an American adult has not had sex in the last year: **1 in 5**

Amount Americans spend annually on pornography: **$11,000,000,000**

Number of obscenity specialists employed by the Department of Justice: **102**

Copies of *Playboy* sold each year per one thousand residents in New York City: **8**

Copies sold per one thousand residents in Des Moines: **22**

Estimated number of pornographic videocassettes that are rented each day: **550,000**

Federal funds spent in 1990 to promote celibacy among teenagers: **$9,500,000**

Rank of sterilization, among the most commonly used methods of birth control in the United States: **1**

Percentage of Americans who say birth control information should be available on television: **78**

Number of condoms used every second in the United States: **14**

Number of lambs needed to make one lambskin condom: **1**

Number of condoms sold in the United States each year, per adult male: **5**

Number sold in Japan each year, per adult male: **11**

Percentage of rural Chinese couples who say they spend less than one minute on foreplay: **34**

Average weight of a Chinese man's testicles, in grams: **19**

Average weight of a Dane's, in grams: **42**

Average length of an erect penis, according to American men, in inches: **10**

Average length, according to American women, in inches: **4**

Average number of sperm per cubic millimeter of an American man's semen in 1929: **100,000,000**

Average number of sperm per cubic millimeter in 1990:
60,000,000

Minimum amount of time it takes a human sperm to reach an
egg, in minutes: **5**

Average number of hours that Americans say they feel "romantic" each day: **1**

Average duration of sexual intercourse for humans, in minutes:
10

Average duration for chimpanzees, in seconds: **10**

Ratio of the size of the female spider monkey's clitoris to the
size of the male monkey's penis: **2:1**

Number of sites on British roads marked to protect toads crossing during the mating season: **357**

Percentage of bird species that are monogamous: **90**

Percentage of mammal species that are: **3**

Percentage of men earning more than fifty thousand dollars a
year who say they have had at least six affairs with coworkers:
20

Average number of sexual fantasies an American man has in
a day: **7**

Average number an American woman has: **3**

Number of orgasms witnessed at the Masters & Johnson Institute in its first nine years of research: **14,000**

Cash prize awarded by a St. Petersburg, Florida, bar to the
winner of its weekly Fake the Big O Contest: **$100**

Percentage of water-bed owners who say that sex is better on one: **33**

Chances that a bed in California is a water bed: **1 in 5**

Rank of "the outdoors" and "trains" among the most popular unconventional places in which Canadians say they've had sex: **1, 2**

Percentage of French women who say they've had sex in a movie theater: **2**

Number of sexual acts depicted in the 270 pages of Bret Easton Ellis's *The Rules of Attraction*: **103**

Percentage of *Redbook* readers who say they would rather have their genitals permanently numbed than go deaf: **70**

Percentage of runners who say they think about sex while running: **66**

Percentage who say they think about running while having sex: **8**

Average number of calories burned during an "extremely passionate" one-minute kiss: **26**

Number of calories in a Hershey's Kiss: **25**

RESOURCES

The sources below are arranged under the headings of the eighty-one categories listed in the table of contents. The numbering corresponds to the order of statistics under each rubric. When a book is cited, our researchers have made every effort to contact the author and verify that the information has not become outdated. When two or more individuals or institutions have worked together to develop a single statistic, each source is listed. A slash indicates that we have combined information provided by disparate sources to create a new statistic. The citation "*Harper's* research" indicates that the magazine's staff has performed significant original research and/or calculation. The statistics in this volume were fact checked between February 1990 and February 1991.

CIVICS

SCHOOL DAYS

1, 2. *Business Week* (N.Y.C.)/
U.S. Department of Labor
(Washington, D.C.)

3. Metropolitan Life Insurance
Company (N.Y.C.)
4. Greater Cleveland Round-
table (Cleveland)
5. National Assessment of Educational Progress (Princeton,
N.J.)
6. Education Commission of

the States (Washington, D.C.)

7–9. Reed Larson, University of Illinois (Urbana)

10. *The New York Times* (Tokyo)

11. United Federation of Teachers (N.Y.C.)

12. National Education Association (Washington, D.C.)

13. U.S. Department of Education (Washington, D.C.)

14. *USA Today* (Arlington, Va.)

15, 16. U.S. Department of Education (Washington, D.C.)

17. Friends for Education (Albuquerque, N.M.)

18. Home School Legal Defense Association (Great Falls, Va.)

19. National Association of Independent Schools (Boston)

20. New York City Board of Education (Brooklyn, N.Y.)

21. Sex Information and Education Council of the United States (N.Y.C.)

22, 23. National Association of State Boards of Education (Alexandria, Va.)

24. Educational Testing Service (Princeton, N.J.)

25. Independent Educational Consultants Association (Forestdale, Mass.)

26. U.S. Bureau of the Census (Washington, D.C.)

27. French for Tots (N.Y.C.)

HIGHER EDUCATION

1. Miss America Pageant (Atlantic City)

2. National Endowment for the Humanities (Washington, D.C.)

3. Christopher Bigsby, University of East Anglia (Norwich, England)

4, 5. Martin K. Starr, Columbia University School of Business (N.Y.C.)

6. National Research Council (Washington, D.C.)

7. Massachusetts Institute of Technology (Cambridge, Mass.)

8, 9. University of Alabama (Tuscaloosa)

10, 11. National Collegiate

Athletic Association (Mission, Kan.)

12, 13. Yale University School of Law (New Haven)

14. Goldfield Mineral Services (London)

15. Trans-American Entertainment (Beverly Hills, Calif.)

16. Harvard University (Cambridge, Mass.)

17. Gallup Organization (Princeton, N.J.)

18. Dale Carnegie and Associates (Garden City, N.Y.)

19. Julie K. Ehrhart and Bernice R. Sandler, Project on the Status and Education of Women of the Association of American Colleges (Washington, D.C.)

20. Donn Byrne, State University of New York (Albany)

21. American Civil Liberties Union (N.Y.C.)

22. National Academy of Sciences (Washington, D.C.)

23. *The Chronicle of Higher Education* (Washington, D.C.)

24. Taco Bell (Irvine, Calif.)

25. American Council of Nanny Schools (University Center, Mich.)

26. Ivor Spencer School (London)

27. Stephen Craddock (Plainfield, Vt.)

29. Dunkin' Donuts Training Center (Braintree, Mass.)

VOTERS AND VOTING

1. U.S. Bureau of the Census (Washington, D.C.)

2. Brian D. Silver, Michigan State University (East Lansing) and Barbara A. Anderson, University of Michigan (Ann Arbor)

3. Brian D. Silver, Michigan State University (East Lansing)

4. 100% Vote–HumanSERVE (N.Y.C.)

5. Republican National Committee (Washington, D.C.)

6. Democratic National Committee (Washington, D.C.)

7. CBS News (N.Y.C.)

8, 9. John Petrocik, University of California (Los Angeles)

10. U.S. Bureau of the Census (Washington, D.C.)

RESOURCES

11. Los Angeles City Clerk's Office (Los Angeles)
12. J&B Scotch–*Spy* Poll (N.Y.C.)
13, 14. Gallup Organization (Princeton, N.J.)
15, 16. Williamsburg Charter Foundation (Washington, D.C.)
17. Ada County Elections Office (Boise, Idaho)

THE CAMPAIGN TRAIL

1. Jay Mathews, *The Washington Post* (Washington, D.C.)/ *Harper's* research (N.Y.C.)
2. Harold Zullow and Martin Seligman, University of Pennsylvania (Philadelphia)/ *Harper's* research (N.Y.C.)
3. Citizens' Research Foundation (Los Angeles)/Commission for the Study of the American Electorate (Washington, D.C.)
4–6. Federal Election Commission (Washington, D.C.)
7. Republican National Committee (Washington, D.C.)

8. Bush Quayle '88 (Washington, D.C.)
9. *The New York Times* (N.Y.C.)
10. *Harper's* research (N.Y.C.)
11. Senator Lloyd Bentsen (Washington, D.C.)
12, 13. Ellen Hume, *The Wall Street Journal* (N.Y.C.)
14, 15. Federal Election Commission (Washington, D.C.)
16. Senator Lloyd Bentsen (Washington, D.C.)
17. Republican National Committee (Washington, D.C.)
18. Democratic National Committee (Washington, D.C.)
19. Dukakis for President (Boston)
20, 21. *U.S. News & World Report* (Washington, D.C.)
22. Federal Election Commission (Washington, D.C.)
23. *Unreliable Sources: A Guide to Detecting Bias in News Media*, by Martin A. Lee (Carol Publishing Group, N.Y.C.)
24. Maura Pierce, *The Washingtonian* (Washington, D.C.)
25. Democratic National Committee (Washington, D.C.)

RESOURCES

26. U.S. Library of Congress (Washington, D.C.)
27. *The Arizona Republic* (Phoenix)
28. Democratic National Committee (Washington, D.C.)
29. Pat Paulsen (Cloverdale, Calif.)

THE CONGRESS

1. *Religion on Capitol Hill*, by Peter Benson and Dorothy Williams (Harper & Row, N.Y.C.)
2. Common Cause (Washington, D.C.)
3. Public Citizen's Congress Watch (Washington, D.C.)
4–6. *Congressional Quarterly* (Washington, D.C.)
7. Senate Judiciary Committee (Washington, D.C.)/*Congressional Quarterly* (Washington, D.C.)
8. Public Citizen's Congress Watch (Washington, D.C.)
9. U.S. House of Representatives Periodical Press Gallery (Washington, D.C.)
10. Senator Tom Harkin (Washington, D.C.)
11. Gordon S. Black Corporation (Rochester, N.Y.)/*USA Today* (Arlington, Va.)
12. CNN poll by Yankelovich Clancy Shulman (Westport, Conn.)
13, 14. Clerk of the U.S. House of Representatives (Washington, D.C.)
15. National Abortion Rights Action League (Washington, D.C.)
16. U.S. Senate Select Committee on Ethics (Washington, D.C.)
17. Clerk of the U.S. House of Representatives (Washington, D.C.)
18. Backer & Spielvogel (N.Y.C.)
19. Representative Dan Glickman (Washington, D.C.)
20–22. *Congressional Insight* (Washington, D.C.)

THE WHITE HOUSE

1. Metropolitan Life Insurance Company (N.Y.C.)

RESOURCES

2. Baseline II (N.Y.C.)
3. Harold G. Maier, Vanderbilt University (Nashville)
4, 5. *Congressional Quarterly* (Washington, D.C.)
6. National Academy of Public Administration (Washington, D.C.)
7. Public Broadcasting Service (Alexandria, Va.)
8, 9. Louis Harris and Associates (N.Y.C.)
10, 11. *People* (N.Y.C.)
12. Playskool (Pawtucket, R.I.)
13. Center for Media and Public Affairs (Washington, D.C.)
14, 15. *New York Times*–CBS News Poll (N.Y.C.)
16. *The National Journal* (Washington, D.C.)
17, 18. Media General (Richmond, Va.)–Associated Press (N.Y.C.) Poll
19. Playskool (Pawtucket, R.I.)

THE COURTS

1. U.S. Department of Justice (Washington, D.C.)
2. U.S. Department of Justice (Highland Park, Md.)

3–5. Sheldon Goldman, University of Massachusetts (Amherst)
6. Federal Judicial Center (Washington, D.C.)
7, 8. Administrative Office of the U.S. Courts (Washington, D.C.)
9. National Security Archive (Washington, D.C.)
10. Legal Services Corporation (Washington, D.C.)
11. National Information Center (Boulder, Colo.)
12, 13. *National Law Journal* (Washington, D.C.)
14, 15. U.S. Library of Congress (Washington, D.C.)
16. Geoffrey Miller, University of Chicago School of Law (Chicago)
17. U.S. Library of Congress (Washington, D.C.)
18, 19. Lawyers Cooperative Publishing Company (Rochester, N.Y.)
20. *American Bar Association Journal* (Washington, D.C.)
21. American Bar Association (Chicago)
22. Rand Corporation (Santa Monica, Calif.)
23. American Bar Association (Chicago)

RESOURCES

24. David A. Kaplan, *Newsweek* (N.Y.C.)
25. Pima County Superior Court (Tucson, Ariz.)
26. Arnold Jacobs, Shea & Gould (N.Y.C.)
27. U.S. Senate Judiciary Committee (Washington, D.C.)
28, 29. *Congressional Quarterly* (Washington, D.C.)
30. U.S. Library of Congress (Washington, D.C.)
31, 32. *Washington Post* Poll (Washington, D.C.)
33. *Harvard Law Review* (Cambridge, Mass.)/*Harper's* research (N.Y.C.)/Edward-Billets Production (Hollywood)

FINES

1. Kenneth Cooper, Knight-Ridder Newspapers (Washington, D.C.)
2, 3. New York City Department of Transportation (N.Y.C.)
4, 5. Franz Spelman, *Time* (Munich, Germany)
6. Deutscher Bundestag (Bonn, Germany)
7. Representative Shelby Rhinehart (Nashville)
8. Flossmoor Police Department (Flossmoor, Ill.)
9. Los Angeles Department of Transportation (Los Angeles)
10. Ravalli County Courthouse (Hamilton, Mont.)
11. Ravalli County Commissioner's Office (Hamilton, Mont.)
12. Virginia State Police Department (Fairfax, Va.)
13. International Fund for Animal Welfare (Yarmouth Port, Mass.)
14. California State Law Library (Sacramento, Ca.)
15. Los Angeles Office of the City Attorney (Los Angeles)
16. Republic of Singapore Police Department (Singapore)

CRIME

1–4. U.S. Department of Justice (Washington, D.C.)
5. Mary P. Koss, University of Arizona (Tucson)

6. Metropolitan Life Insurance Company (N.Y.C.)
7–10. U.S. Department of Justice (Washington, D.C.)
11. Atlantic City Police Department (Atlantic City)
12. *In One Day*, by Tom Parker (Houghton Mifflin, Boston)
13. London House (Park Ridge, Ill.)
14. Peter Berlin Retail Consulting Group (Jericho, N.Y.)
15. U.S. Internal Revenue Service (Washington, D.C.)
16. U.S. Customs Service (Washington, D.C.)
17. Metropolitan Museum of Art (N.Y.C.)
18. International Maritime Bureau (London)
19. Highway Patrol Headquarters (Milford, N.Y.)
20. Iceland State Police (Reykjavík, Iceland)

PUNISHMENT

1. U.S. Bureau of the Census (Washington, D.C.)
2. Charles W. Thomas, University of Florida (Gainesville)
3. U.S. Department of Justice (Washington, D.C.)
4. Roper Organization (N.Y.C.)
5. American Correctional Association (College Park, Md.)
6, 7. U.S. Department of Justice (Washington, D.C.)
8. National Association for the Advancement of Colored People, Legal Defense and Education Fund (N.Y.C.)
9. U.S. Department of Justice (Washington, D.C.)
10. U.S. Bureau of the Census (Washington, D.C.)
11, 12. *From the Yaroslavsky Station*, by Elizabeth Pond (Universe Books, N.Y.C.)
13. South Africa Police Headquarters (Pretoria, South Africa)
14. Zimbabwe Mission to the United Nations (N.Y.C.)
15. Asia Watch (N.Y.C.)
16. CBS News (N.Y.C.)
17. Center for Law and Social Justice (Brooklyn, N.Y.)

RESOURCES

18. American Civil Liberties Union (Washington, D.C.)
19. National Association for the Advancement of Colored People, Legal Defense and Education Fund (N.Y.C.)
20. New York City Department of Correction (N.Y.C.)
21. American Correctional Association (College Park, Md.)
22. United States Attorney's Office (N.Y.C.)
23. Associated Press (N.Y.C.)
24. U.S. Bureau of Prisons (Rochester, Minn.)
25. Office of the Independent Counsel (Washington, D.C.)
26. Beverly Hills Police Department (Beverly Hills, Calif.)

THE DRUG WAR

1. Federal Bureau of Prisons (Washington, D.C.)
2. The White House (Washington, D.C.)
3–5. U.S. Office of Management and Budget (Washington, D.C.)
6. National Institute on Drug Abuse (Rockville, Md.)
7. Drugs and Crime Data Center and Clearinghouse (Washington, D.C.)
8. New York State Division of Substance Abuse Services (Albany)
9. *National Law Journal* (N.Y.C.)
10. National Association of State Boards of Education (Alexandria, Va.)
11, 12. Jack Henningfield, National Institutes on Drug Administration (Baltimore)
13. National Association for Perinatal Addiction Research and Education (Chicago)
14, 15. National Organization for the Reform of Marijuana Laws (Washington, D.C.)
16. Florida State Attorney's Office (Miami)
17, 18. Federal Reserve System (Washington, D.C.)
19. Lee Hearn, Toxicology Testing Service (Miami)
20. Jonathan Marshall, *The Oakland Tribune* (Oakland, Calif.)
21. U.S. Department of State (Washington, D.C.)

22. Ministry of Agriculture (Lima, Peru)
23, 24. Center for Defense Information (Washington, D.C.)
25. Houston Police Department (Houston)
26. U.S. Border Patrol (McAllen, Tex.)
27. *El Espectador* (Bogotá, Colombia)
28. Organismo de Seguridad (Bogotá, Colombia)
29. Washington Office on Latin America (Washington, D.C.)/Andean Commission of Jurists (Lima, Peru)
30. Steven Johnson, *San Jose Mercury News* (San Jose, Calif.)
31. U.S. Customs Service (Washington, D.C.)
32, 33. U.S. Border Patrol (McAllen, Tex.)
34. Interquest Group (Houston)
35. National Organization for the Reform of Marijuana Laws (Washington, D.C.)
36. *Washington Post* (Washington, D.C.)–ABC News (N.Y.C.) Poll

37. SherTest Corporation (Yonkers, N.Y.)
38. Byrd Laboratories (Austin, Tex.)

SECRECY

1. Information Security Oversight Office (Washington, D.C.)
2. U.S. General Accounting Office (Washington, D.C.)
3. Phoenix Field Office of the U.S. Secret Service (Phoenix)
4. David Hooper (London)
5. U.S. General Services Administration (Arlington, Va.)
6–8. Federal Bureau of Investigation (Washington, D.C.)
9. U.S. Internal Revenue Service (Washington, D.C.)
10. U.S. Army Intelligence and Security Command (Fort Belvoir, Va.)
11. U.S. Department of Justice (McLean, Va.)
12. Communication Control Systems of New York (N.Y.C.)

RESOURCES

13. Bensinger, Dupont and Associates (Chicago)
14. U.S. House of Representatives Subcommittee on Health and Long-Term Care (Washington, D.C.)
15. U.S. Internal Revenue Service (Washington, D.C.)
16. McFeely Wackerle Schulman (Chicago)
17. Veterinary Learning Systems (Lawrenceville, N.J.)

SOCIAL STUDIES

THE BATTLE OF THE SEXES

1. U.S. Bureau of the Census (Washington, D.C.)
2, 3. *The Divorce Revolution: The Unexpected Social and Economic Consequences on Women and Children in America*, by Lenore J. Weitzman (Free Press, N.Y.C.)
4, 5. *Time*–CNN Poll by Yankelovich Clancy Shulman (Westport, Conn.)
6, 7. Gallup Organization (Princeton, N.J.)

8, 9. 1990 Virginia Slims Opinion Poll by Roper Organization (N.Y.C.)
10. D.D.B. Needham Worldwide (Chicago)
11. William Frey, University of Minnesota (St. Paul)
12. Milton Kramer, Bethesda Oak Hospital (Cincinnati)
13, 14. Midge Wilson, De Paul University (Chicago)
15. Schmidt Lab Products (Little Falls, N.J.)
16, 17. MRCA Information Services (Stamford, Conn.)
18. Scholl, Incorporated (Memphis)
19, 20. Mark Clements Research (N.Y.C.)
21. Miles Laboratories (Elkhart, Ind.)
22, 23. Roper Organization (N.Y.C.)
24, 25. Michael Hill, University of Nebraska (Lincoln)
26, 27. Lieberman Research (N.Y.C.)
28, 29. Gallup Organization (Princeton, N.J.)
30. Sam Femiano, Men's Studies Association (Northampton, Mass.)

RESOURCES

BLACK AND WHITE

1–3. U.S. Department of Justice (Washington, D.C.)

4. U.S. Senate Judiciary Committee (Washington, D.C.)

5, 6. *Time*–CNN Poll by Yankelovich Clancy Shulman (Westport, Conn.)

7, 8. National Center for Health Statistics (Hyattsville, Md.)

9, 10. Office of the Inspector General (Baltimore)

11, 12. American Association of Suicidology (Denver)

13. Greenberg-Lake: The Analysis Group (Washington, D.C.)

14, 15. U.S. Department of Labor (Washington, D.C.)

16, 17. American Council on Education (Washington, D.C.)

18. *Current Anthropology* (Uxbridge, England)

19. Alpha Phi Alpha Fraternity (Chicago)

20, 21. Media General (Richmond, Va.)–Associated Press (N.Y.C.) Poll

22. National Association of Black Journalists (Orlando)/ Baseball Writers Association (Long Beach, Calif.)

23. *Sports Illustrated* (N.Y.C.)

24. *Readers' Guide to Periodical Literature 1990* (H. W. Wilson, N.Y.C.)

25, 26. Scenic America (Washington, D.C.)

27, 28. Harold Freeman and Colin McCord, Harlem Hospital Center (N.Y.C.)

29. *New York Times*–CBS News Poll (N.Y.C.)

30. Douglas S. Massey, University of Chicago Population Research Center (Chicago)

31. U.S. Bureau of the Census (Washington, D.C.)

32. Joint Center for Political Studies (Washington, D.C.)

33, 34. U.S. Civil Rights Commission (Washington, D.C.)

35–37. National Opinion Research Center (Chicago)

38. U.S. Department of Justice (Washington, D.C.)

39, 40. National Center for Health Statistics (Hyattsville, Md.)

41, 42. National Committee for Adoption (Washington, D.C.)

RESOURCES

43. Child Welfare League (Washington, D.C.)
44. National Opinion Research Center (Chicago)
45. Klanwatch Project of the Southern Poverty Law Center (Montgomery, Ala.)
46. National Center for Health Statistics (Hyattsville, Md.)
47. *The World Almanac and Book of Facts* (Pharos, N.Y.C.)

CHILDHOOD

1, 2. Center for Science in the Public Interest (Washington, D.C.)
3, 4. Jacqueline Eccles, University of Michigan Institute for Social Research (Ann Arbor)
5. George Gerbner, Annenberg School of Communication, University of Pennsylvania (Philadelphia)
6. United Nations Population Division (N.Y.C.)
7. Quaker House (Geneva)
8. Embassy of Israel (Washington, D.C.)

9. Guardian Group (N.Y.C.)
10, 11. American Medical Association (Chicago)/U.S. Bureau of the Census (Washington, D.C.)/ National Center for Health Statistics (Hyattsville, Md.)
12. National Cancer Institute (Bethesda, Md.)
13. Association for Children and Adults with Learning Disabilities (Pittsburgh)
14. *A Basic Vocabulary of Elementary School Children*, by H. D. Rinsland (Macmillan, N.Y.C.)
15. Gary Ingersoll, University of Indiana (Indianapolis)
16. Emanuel Tobier, New York University (N.Y.C.)
17. Jeremy's Place (N.Y.C.)
18. James U. MacNeal, Texas A&M University (College Station)
19, 20. Waldenbooks (Stamford, Conn.)
21. National Injury Information Surveillance System (Bethesda, Md.)
22. U.S. Consumer Product Safety Commission (Washington, D.C.)

RESOURCES

23. Pellettieri, Rabstein & Altman (Princeton, N.J.)
24. Photo Marketing Association (Jackson, Mich.)
25. Nickelodeon Poll by Yankelovich Clancy Shulman (Stamford, Conn.)
26. Search Institute (Minneapolis)

ADOLESCENCE

1, 2. General Dynamics (St. Louis)–National Family Opinion Research (Toledo, Ohio) Poll
3. Smart Services (West Palm Beach, Fla.)
4. Amateur Athletic Union (Indianapolis)
5, 6. D.D.B. Needham Worldwide (N.Y.C.)
7, 8. Greenberg-Lake: The Analysis Group (Washington, D.C.)
9. William Buckley, Pennsylvania State University (University Park)
10. Gary Remafadi, Adolescent Health Program (Minneapolis)

11. Alan Guttmacher Institute (N.Y.C.)
12. New York City Bureau of Health Statistics and Analysis (N.Y.C.)
13. National Center for Health Statistics (Hyattsville, Md.)
14. Federal Bureau of Investigation (Washington, D.C.)
15. Jacqueline Jackson, Rhode Island Rape Crisis Center (Providence, R.I.)
16. Search Institute (Minneapolis)
17. National Center for Health Statistics (Hyattsville, Md.)
18, 19. *Time*–CNN Poll by Yankelovich Clancy Shulman (Westport, Conn.)
20. American Home Economics Association (Washington, D.C.)
21, 22. National Endowment for the Humanities (Washington, D.C.)
23. West Palm Beach County Court House (West Palm Beach, Fla.)
24. American Home Economics Association (Washington, D.C.)
25. Gallup Organization (Princeton, N.J.)

RESOURCES

FADS

1. Hyman Products (St. Louis)
2. Abracadata (Eugene, Ore.)
3. Florida Lottery (Tallahassee, Fla.)
4. R. R. Bowker (N.Y.C.)
5. Freedom Writer (Great Barrington, Mass.)
6. National Climate Data Center (Asheville, N.C.)
7. *Beer Marketers Insights* (West Nyack, N.Y.)
8. Roper Organization (N.Y.C.)
9. Lomma Enterprises (Scranton, Pa.)
10. American Motors Corporation (Detroit)
11. *Des Moines Register* Iowa Poll (Des Moines)
12. Union Products (Leominster, Mass.)
13. *Harper's* research (N.Y.C.)
14. Jay McInerney (N.Y.C.)/ *Harper's* research (N.Y.C.)
15. Universal Esperanto Association (N.Y.C.)
16. Werner Erhard and Associates (San Francisco)
17. The Lempert Company (Belleville, N.J.)

TRADITIONS

1, 2. *Des Moines Register* Iowa Poll (Des Moines)
3. Ivan Muse, Brigham Young University (Provo, Utah)
4. *Texas Monthly* (Austin, Tex.)
5. Roper Organization (N.Y.C.)
6. Beverage Media (N.Y.C.)
7. Tea Council (London)
8. Harry M. Stevens Catering (Louisville, Ky.)
9. U.S. Department of the Interior (Washington, D.C.)
10. Niagara Falls Public Library (Niagara Falls, N.Y.)
11. Spanish National Tourist Board (N.Y.C.)
12. *Reader's Digest* (Pleasantville, N.Y.)
13. National Geographic Society (Washington, D.C.)
14. Smithsonian Institution (Washington, D.C.)
15. *Sex and the American Teenager*, by Robert Coles and Geoffrey Stokes (Harper & Row, N.Y.C.)

RESOURCES

GIVING AND RECEIVING

1. Roper Organization (N.Y.C.)
2, 3. Toy Manufacturers of America (N.Y.C.)
4. Uncle Milton Industries (Culver City, Calif.)
5. Ohio Center for Science and Industry (Columbus, Ohio)
6. New York City Department of Health (N.Y.C.)
7. Embassy of Thailand (Washington, D.C.)
8. Press Office of the Vice-President (Washington, D.C.)
9. Neckwear Association of America (N.Y.C.)
10. Graceland (Memphis)
11, 12. Gallup Organization (Princeton, N.J.)

ords Administration (Washington, D.C.)
5. Tony Bennett Enterprises (N.Y.C.)
6. Solters, Roskin, Friedman (Los Angeles)
7, 8. Florida State University (Tallahassee)
9. *Frank Sinatra: My Father*, by Nancy Sinatra (Burson-Marsteller, Los Angeles)
10–12. Hope Enterprises (Burbank, Calif.)
13. Henny Youngman (N.Y.C.)
14. *Harper's* research (N.Y.C.)
15. "The Joe Franklin Show" (N.Y.C.)
16. Brûlé Ville Associés (Paris)
17. *Advertising Age* (N.Y.C.)
18. *Spy* Poll by Penn and Schoen (N.Y.C.)

MAKING IT BIG

1, 2. Robin Weir (Washington, D.C.)
3. *The Wall Street Journal* (N.Y.C.)
4. National Archives and Rec-

HISTORY

THE REAGAN YEARS

1. Kathleen Day, *The Washington Post* (Washington, D.C.)/

RESOURCES

Office of Ronald Reagan (Los Angeles)

2. Center for Defense Information (Washington, D.C.)

3, 4. U.S. Agency for International Development (Washington, D.C.)/*Harper's* research (N.Y.C.)

5. U.S. Central Intelligence Agency (Washington, D.C.)

6, 7. Citizens for Tax Justice (Washington, D.C.)

8. Jimmy Carter Library (Atlanta)

9, 10. *Hold On, Mr. President!*, by Sam Donaldson (Random House, N.Y.C.)

11. The White House (Washington, D.C.)/Office of Ronald Reagan (Los Angeles)

12. The White House (Washington, D.C.)

13, 14. U.S. Department of Defense (Washington, D.C.)

15. U.S. General Accounting Office (Washington, D.C.)/Federal Procurement Data Center (Washington, D.C.)

16. U.S. General Accounting Office (Washington, D.C.)

17. *Time* Poll by Yankelovich Clancy Shulman (Westport, Conn.)

18. *U.S. News & World Report* (Washington, D.C.)

19. *The Washington Post* (Washington, D.C.)

20. *Divorcing the Dictator*, by Frederick Kempe (Putnam, N.Y.C.)

21, 22. Benjamin Weiser, *The Washington Post* (Washington, D.C.)

23. Fred Barnes, *The New Republic* (Washington, D.C.)

24. *Harper's* research (N.Y.C.)

25. J&B Scotch–*Spy* Poll (N.Y.C.)

26. Herman Goelitz Candy Company (Fairfield, Calif.)

27, 28. *Who's Who in America* (Macmillan, Wilmette, Ill.)

29. U.S. General Services Administration (Washington, D.C.)

THE GORBACHEV LEGACY

1. *Harper's* research (N.Y.C.)

2. Harvard University (Cambridge, Mass.)

3. *The New York Times* (Moscow)

4. Tass (N.Y.C.)

RESOURCES

5. Czechoslovak News Agency (N.Y.C.)
6. *Gazeta Wyborcza* (Warsaw)
7. Consulate of Poland (Washington, D.C.)
8, 9. Planecon (Washington, D.C.)
10. Embassy of Germany (Washington, D.C.)
11. Donaldson, Lufkin & Jenrette (N.Y.C.)/*Harper's* research (N.Y.C.)
12. Russian Dressing (N.Y.C.)
13. *The New York Times* (N.Y.C.)
14, 15. Martilla & Kiley (Boston)
16. Du Pont (Wilmington, Del.)/E. S. Gordon Company (N.Y.C.)
17, 18. *Gazeta International* (Warsaw)
19. Central Association of West German House, Apartment and Real Estate Owners (Düsseldorf, Germany)
20, 21. *Der Spiegel* (Hamburg, Germany)
22. *U.S. News & World Report* (Washington, D.C.)
23. Embassy of the Soviet Union (Washington, D.C.)
24. Institute for East-West Security Studies (N.Y.C.)
25. U.S. Department of State (Washington, D.C.)
26. *Krazsnaya Zvezda* (Moscow)
27. Embassy of India (Washington, D.C.)
28. Polish Interpress Agency (Warsaw)
29. *Gazeta International* (Warsaw)
30. Intersex (Warsaw)
31. *The New York Times* (Moscow)
32. "Late Night with David Letterman" (N.Y.C.)

MILITARY AFFAIRS

1. James Clayton, University of Utah (Salt Lake City)
2. James Clayton, University of Utah (Salt Lake City)/Federal Reserve Board (Washington, D.C.)
3. Center for Defense Information (Washington, D.C.)
4. *The National Journal* (Washington, D.C.)
5. Federal Procurement Data System (Washington, D.C.)
6, 7. General Dynamics (St. Louis)
8. U.S. Department of Veter-

RESOURCES

ans Affairs (Washington, D.C.)

9. U.S. Departments of the Navy, Air Force and Marines (Washington, D.C.)

10, 11. Defense Personnel Support Center (Philadelphia)

12, 13. U.S. Department of Defense (Washington, D.C.)

14. U.S. Department of the Air Force (Washington, D.C.)

15. U.S. Department of Defense (Washington, D.C.)

16. U.S. Department of the Navy (Washington, D.C.)

17. U.S. Department of Defense (Washington, D.C.)

18. Air Logistics Center, Kelly Air Force Base (San Antonio)

19. National Institute of Standards and Technology (Gaithersburg, Md.)

20. U.S. Department of the Air Force (Washington, D.C.)

21. U.S. Congressional Budget Office (Washington, D.C.)

22. U.S. Department of the Air Force (Washington, D.C.)

23. U.S. Department of the Army (Alexandria, Va.)

24. U.S. Department of Defense (Washington, D.C.)

25. K mart (Hinesville, Ga.)

MILITARY PERSONNEL

1. Ralph Estes, American University (Washington, D.C.)

2, 3. U.S. Department of Veterans Affairs (Washington, D.C.)

4. U.S. General Accounting Office (Washington, D.C.)

5. U.S. Department of Defense (Washington, D.C.)

6. Hasbro Inc. (Pawtucket, R.I.)/U.S. Department of Defense (Washington, D.C.)

7, 8. U.S. Department of the Navy (Arlington, Va.)

9. U.S. Department of Defense (Washington, D.C.)

10. U.S. Military Academy (West Point, N.Y.)

11, 12. U.S. Department of the Air Force (Washington, D.C.)

13. U.S. General Accounting Office (Washington, D.C.)

14. *Time* (Washington, D.C.)

15, 16. U.S. Department of Defense (Washington, D.C.)

17. U.S. Department of Defense (Washington, D.C.)/ U.S. General Accounting Office (Washington, D.C.)
18. Naval Ocean Systems Center (San Diego)
19. U.S. General Accounting Office (Washington, D.C.)
20. American Manufacturers Export Group (Houston)
21. Bugmasters Incorporated (Columbia, Md.)

WEAPONRY

1. Wright-Patterson Air Force Base (Dayton, Ohio)
2. Natural Resources Defense Council (Washington, D.C.)
3. Roper Organization (N.Y.C.)
4, 5. U.S. Department of Energy (Washington, D.C.)
6, 7. Federation of American Scientists (Washington, D.C.)
8. Center for Defense Information (Washington, D.C.)
9. Anniston Army Depot (Anniston, Ala.)
10, 11. Arms Control and Dis-

armament Agency (Washington, D.C.)
12, 13. U.S. Congressional Research Service (Washington, D.C.)
14. Freedom House (Washington, D.C.)
15. Office of the Registrar General (Port Stanley, Falkland Islands)
16. British Crossbow Society (Derby, England)
17. U.S. Bureau of Alcohol, Tobacco and Firearms (Washington, D.C.)
18. *Time*–CNN Poll by Yankelovich Clancy Shulman (Westport, Conn.)
19. American Historical Foundation (Richmond, Va.)
20. Center for Defense Information (Washington, D.C.)
21. U.S. Department of Labor (Washington, D.C.)/Center for Defense Information (Washington, D.C.)

CASUALTIES OF WAR

1, 2. William Eckhardt, Lentz Peace Research Laboratory (Dunedin, Fla.)

RESOURCES

3, 4. Rand Corporation (Santa Monica, Calif.)

5. U.S. Department of State (Washington, D.C.)

6. International Committee of the Red Cross (Geneva)

7. *The Clothes Have No Emperor: A Chronicle of the American '80s* by Paul Slansky (Fireside/Simon & Schuster, N.Y.C.)/Facts on File (N.Y.C.)

8, 9. U.S. Department of Defense (Washington, D.C.)

10. Embassy of Nicaragua (Washington, D.C.)/U.S. Department of Defense (Washington, D.C.)

11. Stanley Karnow (Potomac, Md.)/Vietnam Veterans Memorial (Washington, D.C.)

12. U.S. Department of Veterans Affairs (Washington, D.C.)

13, 14. U.S. Department of Defense (Washington, D.C.)

15. Robert Lewis, Columbia University (N.Y.C.)

16, 17. U.S. Department of State (Washington, D.C.)

18, 19. Carter Center, Emory University (Atlanta)

20, 21. William Eckhardt, Lentz Peace Research Laboratory (Dunedin, Fla.)

DÉJÀ VU

1. 70's Preservation Society (N.Y.C.)

2. Beer Can Collectors Association (Fenton, Mo.)

3. Steve Jenne (Springfield, Ill.)

4. National Archives and Records Administration (Washington, D.C.)

5. U.S. Peace Corps (Washington, D.C.)

6. Shelby County Sheriff's Office (Memphis)

7. Christi Phillips (N.Y.C.)

8. Cheryl J. Lewin Associates (Chicago)

9. Benjamin Zablocki, Rutgers University (New Brunswick, N.J.)

10. Paul Hudson, Oglethorpe University (Atlanta)

11. *Rolling Stone* (N.Y.C.)

12. *TV Guide* (Radnor, Pa.)

13. Viacom Productions (Los Angeles)

14. Broadcast Music Incorporated (N.Y.C.)

15. *Mindworks: Time and Conscious Experience*, by Ernst Pöppel (Harcourt Brace Jovanovich, N.Y.C.)

16. *Innumeracy: Mathematical*

Illiteracy and Its Consequences, by John Allen Paulos (Farrar Straus Giroux, N.Y.C.)

17. Gallup Organization (Princeton, N.J.)

GEOGRAPHY

STATE OF THE WORLD

1. Albert P. Blaustein, Rutgers University School of Law (Camden, N.J.)
2. United Nations (N.Y.C.)
3. U.S. Department of State (Washington, D.C.)
4. Freedom House (N.Y.C.)
5. World Bank (Washington, D.C.)
6. Amnesty International (N.Y.C.)
7. Rand Corporation (Santa Monica, Calif.)
8. United Nations (N.Y.C.)
9, 10. U.S. Mission to the United Nations (N.Y.C.)
11, 12. William Eckhardt, Lentz Peace Research Laboratory (Dunedin, Fla.)

13. *Maclean's* (Toronto)
14. National Geographic Society Poll by the Gallup Organization (Princeton, N.J.)
15, 16. American Council of Teachers of Russian (Washington, D.C.)
17. Michael Kraus, University of Alaska (Fairbanks)
18. J. Mayone Stycos, Cornell University (Ithaca, N.Y.)
19. Planned Parenthood Federation of America Poll by Louis Harris and Associates (N.Y.C.)
20. Population Reference Bureau (Washington, D.C.)
21. *Hindustan Times* (New Delhi)
22. U.S. Agency for International Development (Washington, D.C.)
23. National Organization for Women (Washington, D.C.)
24. U.S. Department of State (Washington, D.C.)
25. *Harper's* research (N.Y.C.)
26. Harcourt Brace Jovanovich (N.Y.C.)
27, 28. U.S. Committee for

RESOURCES

Refugees (Washington, D.C.)
29. University of California Deep Sea Drilling Project (San Diego)
30. Maharishi International University (Fairfield, Iowa)

LATIN AMERICA

1. Instituto Histórico Centroamericano (Managua, Nicaragua)
2. United Nations (N.Y.C.)
3. Inter-American Development Bank (Washington, D.C.)
4. Nicaragua Network (Washington, D.C.)
5. U.S. General Services Administration (Washington, D.C.)
6. U.S. Senate Library (Washington, D.C.)
7. *Washington Post* (Washington, D.C.)–ABC News (N.Y.C.) Poll
8. Central American Historical Institute (Washington, D.C.)
9. U.S. Catholic Conference (Washington, D.C.)

10. Washington Office on Latin America (Washington, D.C.)
11. Center for Defense Information (Washington, D.C.)
12. Angelo M. Codevilla, Stanford University (Palo Alto, Calif.)
13. *Jornal do Brasil* (Rio de Janeiro)
14. Brazilian Institute for Geography and Statistics (Rio de Janeiro)
15. Lawrence Weschler, *Columbia Journalism Review* (N.Y.C.)
16. Embassy of Peru (Washington, D.C.)
17. Carter Center, Emory University (Atlanta)
18. Nicaragua Network (Washington, D.C.)
19, 20. U.S. Department of State (Washington, D.C.)
21. Brazilian Institute for Geography and Statistics (Rio de Janeiro)
22. Guatemalan Human Rights Commission (Washington, D.C.)
23. Leah Carroll, University of California (Berkeley)

RESOURCES

24–26. U.S. Congressional Arms Control and Foreign Policy Caucus (Washington, D.C.)

27. Market Opinion Research (Washington, D.C.)

28, 29. Times Mirror Center for the People and the Press (Washington, D.C.)

30. Council on Hemispheric Affairs (Washington, D.C.)

31. U.S. Embassy in El Salvador (San Salvador)

32. Leah Carroll, University of California (Berkeley)

33. Washington Office on Latin America (Washington, D.C.)/Andean Commission of Jurists (Lima, Peru)

34. Leah Carroll, University of California (Berkeley)

35. Rodrigo Rojas Fund (Washington, D.C.)

36. Americas Watch (N.Y.C.)

37. Washington Office on Latin America (Washington, D.C.)

38. Baseball for Peace (Davis, Calif.)

39, 40. U.S. Department of State (Washington, D.C.)

THE MIDDLE EAST

1. U.S. Arms Control and Disarmament Agency (Washington, D.C.)

2. U.S. Agency for International Development (Washington, D.C.)

3. Ruth Leger Sivard, World Priorities (Washington, D.C.)

4. U.S. Department of Energy (Washington, D.C.)/U.S. Department of Defense (Washington, D.C.)

5, 6. World Bank (Washington, D.C.)

7. Palestinian Human Rights Information Center (Chicago)

8. Embassy of Israel (Washington, D.C.)

9. Palestinian Human Rights Information Center (Chicago)

10–14. Consulate of Israel (N.Y.C.)

15. *Universal Almanac 1991*, edited by John W. Wright (Andrews & McMeel, Kansas City)

16. U.S. Bureau of the Census (Washington, D.C.)

17. *The Economist* (London)
18. United Nations (N.Y.C.)/ Center for Defense Information (Washington, D.C.)
19. U.S. Arms Control and Disarmament Agency (Washington, D.C.)
20. Times Mirror Center for the People and the Press (Washington, D.C.)
21. U.S. Department of Agriculture (Washington, D.C.)
22. *Des Moines Register* Iowa Poll (Des Moines)
23. Fairness & Accuracy in Reporting (N.Y.C.)
24. U.S. Department of State (Washington, D.C.)
25. DataBase Project on Palestinian Human Rights (Chicago)
26. Embassy of Israel (Washington, D.C.)
27. Roper Organization (N.Y.C.)
28. *Harper's* research (N.Y.C.)
29. Deborah Amos, *Mother Jones* (San Francisco)
30. *Le Parisien* (Paris)
31. ASR Corporation (Cupertino, Calif.)
32, 33. *Al-Medina* (Jidda, Saudi Arabia)

JAPAN

1. Embassy of Japan (Washington D.C.)/U.S. Agency for International Development (Washington, D.C.)
2. Embassy of Japan (Washington, D.C.)
3. Japanese Playing Corporation (Tokyo)
4. Embassy of Japan (N.Y.C.)
5. Bank of Japan (N.Y.C.)
6. Federal Reserve Bank of San Francisco (San Francisco)
7. U.S. Department of Commerce (Washington, D.C.)
8. *The Wall Street Journal* (Tokyo)
9. Natural Resources Defense Council (N.Y.C.)
10, 11. Southland Corporation (Dallas)
12. Japan Council of Shopping Centers (Tokyo)
13. *Washington Report* (St. Petersburg, Fla.)
14. Honda (N.Y.C.)/Nissan (N.Y.C.)/Toyota (N.Y.C.)
15. Chrysler Corporation (Highland Park, Mich.)/Ford Motor Company (Dearborn, Mich.)/General Motors Corporation (Detroit)

RESOURCES

16. United Auto Workers (Detroit)
17. Yoshi Tsurumi, Baruch College, City University of New York (N.Y.C.)
18. Japanese Ministry of Labor (Tokyo)
19, 20. Citizens for Tax Justice (Washington, D.C.)
21. U.S. Department of Commerce (Washington, D.C.)
22. Senator Jim Sasser (Washington, D.C.)
23. Embassy of Japan (Washington, D.C.)
24. Massachusetts Institute of Technology (Cambridge, Mass.)
25. Liceo Mexicano Japonés (Mexico City)/Embassy of Mexico (Washington, D.C.)
26. *The New York Times* (Tokyo)
27. *The New York Times* (N.Y.C.)
28. *Asahi Shimbun Weekly* (Tokyo)
29. Mitsukoshi department store (Tokyo)
30. General Mills (Minneapolis)

MIGRATION

1. Golin-Harris (Chicago)
2. Population Reference Bureau (Arlington, Va.)/U.S. Bureau of the Census (Washington, D.C.)
3. Lawyers Committee for Human Rights (N.Y.C.)
4. U.S. Department of Justice (Washington, D.C.)
5–7. U.S. Immigration and Naturalization Service (Washington, D.C.)
8. Leo Estrada, University of California (Los Angeles)
9. Population Reference Bureau (Arlington, Va.)/U.S. Bureau of the Census (Washington, D.C.)
10. U.S. Department of State (Washington, D.C.)
11–15. U.S. Immigration and Naturalization Service (Washington, D.C.)
16. Consulate of Israel (N.Y.C.)
17. Consulate of South Africa (Washington, D.C.)
18. Embassy of South Africa (Washington, D.C.)
19. U.S. Department of State (Washington, D.C.)

RESOURCES

20. United Nations High Commissioner on Refugees (N.Y.C.)

TRANSPORTATION

1. Worldwatch Institute (Washington, D.C.)
2. Fortino and Associates (Pittsburgh)
3. California State Assembly (Sacramento, Calif.)
4, 5. Orange County Coroner's Office (Santa Ana, Calif.)
6. U.S. Department of Transportation (Washington, D.C.)
7. American Airlines (Dallas)
8, 9. Federal Aviation Administration (Washington, D.C.)
10, 11. Airline Economics (Washington, D.C.)
12. Professional Airways Systems Specialists (Washington, D.C.)
13. Rocky Mountain Institute (Snowmass, Colo.)/*Harper's* research (N.Y.C.)
14. California Department of Motor Vehicles (Sacramento, Calif.)
15. Rhode Island Department of Motor Vehicles (Providence, R.I.)
16. U.S. General Accounting Office (Washington, D.C.)
17. Loners on Wheels (Fort Worth)
18. *Des Moines Register* Iowa Poll (Des Moines)
19. Volkswagen of America (Troy, Mich.)
20. Campbell Soup Company (Camden, N.J.)
21–23. Runzheimer International (Rochester, Wis.)
24. CCC Information Services (Chicago)
25, 26. *Spy* (N.Y.C.)
27. Rolls-Royce Motor Cars (Cheshire, England)
28. *The Australian* (Sydney)
29, 30. U.S. Bureau of the Census (Washington, D.C.)
31. *Los Angeles Times* (Los Angeles)
32. U.S. Bureau of the Census (Washington, D.C.)
33. Rails to Trails Conservancy (Washington, D.C.)

34. Association of American Railroads (Washington, D.C.)/*Trains* (Milwaukee)
35. R. L. Polk & Company (Detroit)
36. U.S. Department of Transportation (Washington, D.C.)
37. *Roman Empire, 27 B.C.– A.D. 476: A Study in Survival,* by Chester Starr (Oxford University Press, N.Y.C.)
38. U.S. Department of Transportation (Washington, D.C.)
39, 40. R. H. Bruskin Associates (New Brunswick, N.J.)

NEW YORK, NEW YORK

1. New York City Transit Authority (Brooklyn, N.Y.)
2, 3. Joseph Berman Realty (Brooklyn, N.Y.)
4. New York City Department of Sanitation (N.Y.C.)
5. New York City Police Department (Bronx, N.Y.)
6. Sidewalks of New York (N.Y.C.)
7. *The New York Times* (N.Y.C.)
8, 9. New York City Police Department (N.Y.C.)
10. Screen Actors Guild (Los Angeles)
11, 12. CBS (N.Y.C.)
13. League of New York Theatres and Producers (N.Y.C.)
14. New York City Department of Sanitation (N.Y.C.)
15. Port Authority of New York and New Jersey (N.Y.C.)
16, 17. New York City Department of Health (N.Y.C.)
18. New York City Tree Consortium (N.Y.C.)
19. Van de Wetering (Wading River, N.Y.)
20. CACI Marketing Systems (Fairfax, Va.)
21. New York Telephone (N.Y.C.)
22, 23. New York City Transit Authority (N.Y.C.)
24. Rich Temple (N.Y.C.)
25. Nester's Map and Guide Corporation (N.Y.C.)

RESOURCES

SOUTHERN HOSPITALITY

1–3. U.S. Bureau of the Census (Washington, D.C.)
4. National Association for the Advancement of Colored People, Legal Aid Education Fund (Atlanta)
5. National Association for the Advancement of Colored People, Legal Defense and Education Fund (N.Y.C.)
6. Florida Department of Corrections (Tallahassee, Fla.)
7. Gallup Organization (Princeton, N.J.)
8. Broward County Medical Examiner (Fort Lauderdale, Fla.)
9. *Environmental Engineering News* (Lafayette, Ind.)
10. National Association for the Advancement of Colored People (Atlanta)
11. *Atlanta Journal and Constitution* Southern Poll (Atlanta)
12. CBS News Poll (N.Y.C.)
13. Highland Park Building Inspection Department (Highland Park, Tex.)
14. Texas Restaurant Association (Dallas)
15. International Association of Ice Cream Manufacturers (Washington, D.C.)
16. Maurice's Gourmet Barbecue at Piggie Park (Columbia, S.C.)
17. Jefferson Parish Sewage (Harahan, La.)
18. Jon Rooney, Oklahoma State University (Stillwater)
19. Representative Tom Keegan (Columbia, S.C.)
20. Ziegler Music (Baton Rouge, La.)

AMERICAN PIE

1. National Research Bureau (Chicago)
2. Frank J. Popper, Rutgers University (New Brunswick, N.J.)
3. U.S. Bureau of the Census (Washington, D.C.)
4. City Clerk's Office (Britt, Iowa)
5–7. U.S. Bureau of the Census (Washington, D.C.)
8. Benevolent and Protective Order of Elks (Bismarck,

N.D.)/U.S. Bureau of the Census (Washington, D.C.)

9. Victor McKusick, Johns Hopkins University School of Medicine (Baltimore)

10. *Des Moines Register* Iowa Poll (Des Moines)

11. Kiwanis International (Indianapolis)

12. Abraham Lincoln Association (Springfield, Ill.)

13. Calvin Coolidge Memorial Foundation (Plymouth, Vt.)

14. Gallup Organization (London)

15. *The European Discovery of America*, by Samuel Morison (Oxford University Press, N.Y.C.)

16, 17. U.S. Bureau of the Census (Washington, D.C.)

18. U.S. Geological Survey (Reston, Va.)

19. Roper Organization (N.Y.C.)

20. David Wolper Productions (Burbank, Calif.)

21. Dettra Flag Company (Oaks, Pa.)

22, 23. Playskool (Pawtucket, R.I.)

COMMUNICATIONS

NEWS

1. Committee to Protect Journalists (N.Y.C.)

2. Luis Reyes, *Panahon* (Masbate Island, Philippines)

3. *The Washington Post* (Washington, D.C.)

4. *Harper's* research (N.Y.C.)

5, 6. Center for Media and Public Affairs (Washington, D.C.)

7. Essential Information (Washington, D.C.)

8. Fairness & Accuracy in Reporting (N.Y.C.)/*Harper's* research (N.Y.C.)

9. "Nightline" (N.Y.C.)

10. "NBC Nightly News" (N.Y.C.)

11. *The Washington Post* (Washington, D.C.)

12. Audit Bureau of Circulations (Chicago)/Hudson News Corporation (N.Y.C.)/ *Manhattan, inc.* (N.Y.C.)

13. Soviet Press Information (Washington, D.C.)

14. Magazine Publishers Association (N.Y.C.)

RESOURCES

15, 16. Bernadette Barker-Plumber, University of Pennsylvania (Philadelphia)

17. U.S. Department of Justice (Washington, D.C.)

18. Associated Press (N.Y.C.)

19. *Quayle Quarterly* (Bridgeport, Conn.)/*Harper's* research (N.Y.C.)

20. Kiku Adatto, Harvard University (Cambridge, Mass.)

21. The Times Mirror Poll (Washington, D.C.)

22. Bruce Sanford, Baker and Hostetler (Washington, D.C.)

23. *Reader's Guide to Periodical Literature 1961* (H. W. Wilson, N.Y.C.)

24. *Reader's Guide to Periodical Literature 1990* (H. W. Wilson, N.Y.C.)

25. *Spy* (N.Y.C.)

THE TUBE

1. Roper Organization (N.Y.C.)

2. U.S. Bureau of the Census (Washington, D.C.)

3, 4. Roper Organization (N.Y.C.)

5. Mary Story and Patricia Faulkner, University of Minnesota (Minneapolis)

6. Video Storyboard Tests (N.Y.C.)

7. Fox Network (N.Y.C.)

8. A. C. Nielsen Media Research (N.Y.C.)

9. Jay Martel, *Rolling Stone* (N.Y.C.)

10. Saatchi & Saatchi (N.Y.C.)

11. George Gerbner, Annenberg School of Communications, University of Pennsylvania (Philadelphia)

12. "Late Night with David Letterman" (N.Y.C.)

13. *Harper's* research (N.Y.C.)

14, 15. Roper Organization (N.Y.C.)

16. Sherwood Schwartz (Los Angeles)

17. "P.M. Magazine" (San Francisco)

18, 19. Media General (Richmond, Va.)–Associated Press (N.Y.C.) Poll

20. Edward Zwick, Bedford Falls Company (Studio City, Calif.)

21. MGM-Pathé Communications, by A. C. Nielsen Media Research (Northbrook, Ill.)
22. A. C. Nielsen Media Research (N.Y.C.)
23. Brite Voice Systems (Wichita, Kan.)
24. World Vision Enterprises (N.Y.C.)
25. Lorimar Television (Culver City, Calif.)
26. *The Journal of Communication* (Philadelphia)
27. Planned Parenthood Federation of America (N.Y.C.)
28, 29. *Harper's* research (N.Y.C.)

HOLLYWOOD

1. Motion Picture Association of America (N.Y.C.)
2. Academy of Motion Picture Arts and Sciences (Beverly Hills, Calif.)
3. National Association of Theater Owners (Los Angeles)
4. *International Motion Picture Almanac 1990* (Quigley, N.Y.C.)
5. *Variety* (Los Angeles)
6. Academy of Motion Picture Arts and Sciences (Beverly Hills, Calif.)
7. Writers Guild of America (West Hollywood, Calif.)
8. *Business Week* (N.Y.C.)
9. United Nations Educational, Scientific and Cultural Organization (Paris)
10. Walt Disney Pictures (Burbank, Calif.)
11. Amblin Entertainment (Universal City, Calif.)
12. Cinema Secrets (Burbank, Calif.)
13, 14. *Harper's* research (N.Y.C.)
15, 16. Daniel Linz, University of California (Santa Barbara)
17. Maureen Dowd, *The New York Times Magazine* (N.Y.C.)
18. George Steinbrenner (Ft. Meyers, Fla.)
19. California Film Office (Hollywood)
20–23. *Harper's* research (N.Y.C.)
24. Erol's (Springfield, Va.)
25. Frederick's of Hollywood (Hollywood)
26. Collectors Book Store (Hollywood)

RESOURCES

27. *Harper's* research (N.Y.C.)
28. New Line Cinema (N.Y.C.)
29. Surge Licensing (Jericho, N.Y.)
30. Universal Studios Tour (Universal City, Calif.)
31, 32. *Harper's* research (N.Y.C.)

MUSIC

1. Roper Organization (N.Y.C.)
2. *Des Moines Register* Iowa Poll (Des Moines)
3. American Accordion Association (N.Y.C.)
4. Jensen Publications (Milwaukee)
5. David M. Lipscomb, University of Tennessee (Knoxville)
6. *The New Book of People*, by Christopher Anderson (Putnam, N.Y.C.)
7. *Rolling Stone* (N.Y.C.)/*Harper's* research (N.Y.C.)
8. John Scott, DeadBase (Hanover, N.Y.)
9. Massachusetts National Guard (Reading, Mass.)
10. U.S. Department of Education (Washington, D.C.)
11. *Wigwag* (N.Y.C.)
12. *Des Moines Register* Iowa Poll (Des Moines)
13. Casey Kasem (Culver City, Calif.)
14. WXTB Radio (Clearwater, Fla.)
15. Muzak (Seattle)
16. McGavren Guild Radio (N.Y.C.)
17. Miller, Kaplan, Arase & Company (Hollywood)
18, 19. Radio Information Center (N.Y.C.)
20. Graceland (Memphis)
21. Peter Newcomb, *Forbes* (N.Y.C.)
22. *Harper's* research (N.Y.C.)
23. National Association of Jazz Educators (Manhattan, Kan.)
24, 25. *Des Moines Register* Iowa Poll (Des Moines)
26. Gavin Edwards, *Spin* (N.Y.C.)
27. *Backstreets* (Seattle)
28–30 Parents' Music Resource Center (Arlington, Va.)
31. Recording Industry Association of America (Washington, D.C.)
32–34. Loraine Prinsky and Jill

239

RESOURCES

Rosenbaum, California State University (Fullerton)

READING AND WRITING

1. Committee to Protect Journalists (N.Y.C.)
2, 3. Viking Penguin (London)
4. Ariel Dorfman, Duke University (Durham, S.C.)
5. Signet Classics (N.Y.C.)
6. Maureen Dowd, *The New York Times* (Washington, D.C.)
7. *Harper's* research (N.Y.C.)
8. *Spy* (N.Y.C.)/*Harper's* research (N.Y.C.)
9. *Harper's* research (N.Y.C.)
10, 11. Times Mirror Center for the People and the Press (Washington, D.C.)
12. National Assessment of Education Progress (Princeton, N.J.)
13. Princeton Review (N.Y.C.)
14. *World Book Encyclopedia* (World Book, Inc., Chicago)
15, 16. *Oxford English Dictionary* (Clarendon Press, Oxford, England)

17. *The Slang and Jargon of Drunks and Drink,* by Richard A. Spears (Scarecrow Press, Metuchen, N.J.)
18. Oxford University Press (N.Y.C.)
19. Carlin Romano, *The National Book Critics Circle Journal* (Philadelphia)
20. Rod McKuen (Beverly Hills, Calif.)
21. *Romantic Times* (Brooklyn, N.Y.)
22. Swan Publishing (Placentia, Calif.)
23. *College Store Executive* (Westbury, N.Y.)
24. *Spy* (N.Y.C.)
25, 26. *Harper's* research (N.Y.C.)
27. Delacorte Press (N.Y.C.)
28, 29. *Innumeracy: Mathematical Illiteracy and Its Consequences,* by John Allen Paulos (Farrar Straus Giroux, N.Y.C.)

IN THE MAIL

1. U.S. Postal Service (Washington, D.C.)

RESOURCES

2. Direct Marketing Association (N.Y.C.)
3. Thoreau Society (Concord, Mass.)
4. Graceland (Memphis)
5. Hallmark Cards (Kansas City, Mo.)
6. Simmons Market Research (N.Y.C.)
7. Greeting Card Association (Washington, D.C.)
8, 9. U.S. Postal Service (Washington, D.C.)
10. Joel Ehrenkranz, Franklin Diagnostics (Morristown, N.J.)
11–13. U.S. Postal Service (Washington, D.C.)

ON THE PHONE

1. American Telephone and Telegraph Company (Basking Ridge, N.J.)
2. Communications Fraud Control Association (McLean, Va.)
3. Consumer Federation of America (Washington, D.C.)

4. South Central Bell (Jackson, Miss.)
5. New York Telephone (N.Y.C.)
6. United Telecom (Kansas City, Mo.)/Charles Berlitz (Ft. Lauderdale, Fla.)
7. Institute for Democracy in Eastern Europe (N.Y.C.)
8. Palestine Human Rights Information Center (Chicago)
9. U.S. Consumer Product Safety Commission (Washington, D.C.)
10. Magikcity Media (Miami)
11. The White House (Washington, D.C.)
12. District of Columbia Police Department (Washington, D.C.)
13, 14. Southwestern Bell Telephone (St. Louis)

ECONOMICS

WEALTH AND POVERTY

1. *Financial World* (N.Y.C.)
2. Consumer Federation of

America (Washington, D.C.)

3. Roper Organization (N.Y.C.)

4. U.S. Congressional Joint Economic Committee (Washington, D.C.)

5. Federal Reserve System (Washington, D.C.)

6, 7. Citizens for Tax Justice (Washington, D.C.)

8. Sheldon Danziger, University of Michigan (Ann Arbor)

9. Gallup Organization (London)

10. *Forbes* (N.Y.C.)

11. Children's Defense Fund (Washington, D.C.)

12. U.S. Bureau of the Census (Washington, D.C.)

13, 14. Food and Hunger Hotline (N.Y.C.)

15. "21" Club (N.Y.C.)

16, 17. *How You Rate: Men*, by Tom Biracree (Dell, N.Y.C.)

18. National Opinion Research Center (Chicago)

19. Coalition for the Homeless (N.Y.C.)

20. U.S. Department of Labor (Washington, D.C.)

21. Federal Reserve System (Washington, D.C.)

22. Andrew Hacker, City University of New York (Queens)/*Harper's* research (N.Y.C.)

23. *Fortune* (N.Y.C.)

24. *Limousine and Chauffeur Magazine* (Redondo Beach, Calif.)

25. Donald Trump (N.Y.C.)

26, 27. *The Wall Street Journal* (N.Y.C.)

TAXES

1. *The New York Times* (N.Y.C.)/*Harper's* research (N.Y.C.)

2. *Washington Post* (Washington, D.C.)–ABC News (N.Y.C.) Poll

3. Tax Foundation (Washington, D.C.)

4. Center on Budget and Policy Priorities (Washington, D.C.)

5. U.S. Internal Revenue Service (Washington, D.C.)

6. Citizens for Tax Justice (Washington, D.C.)

7, 8. Eagle Eye Publishers (Arlington, Va.)

9. Senator David L. Boren (Washington, D.C.)
10, 11. U.S. Congressional Budget Office (Washington, D.C.)
12. U.S. Office of Management and Budget (Washington, D.C.)
13–15. U.S. Internal Revenue Service (Washington, D.C.)
16. U.S. General Accounting Office (Washington, D.C.)
17, 18. H&R Block (Kansas City, Mo.)/*Harper's* research (N.Y.C.)

IOUs

1. U.S. Department of the Treasury (Washington, D.C.)/*Harper's* research (N.Y.C.)
2. U.S. Office of Management and Budget (Washington, D.C.)
3, 4. U.S. Bureau of the Census (Washington, D.C.)
5–7. Federal Reserve System (Washington, D.C.)
8. Roper Organization (N.Y.C.)
9. U.S. Department of the Treasury (Washington, D.C.)
10, 11. Moody's Investors Service (N.Y.C.)
12. Comstock Partners (N.Y.C.)
13, 14. Federal Reserve System (Washington, D.C.)
15. U.S. Congressional Budget Office (Washington, D.C.)
16. International Monetary Fund (Washington, D.C.)
17. World Bank (Washington, D.C.)
18. Conservation International (Washington, D.C.)
19. Peruvian Ministry of Trade (Lima, Peru)

IMPORTS AND EXPORTS

1. IBM (Armonk, N.Y.)
2. U.S. Department of Commerce (Washington, D.C.)
3, 4. Organization for Economic Cooperation and Development (Paris)
5, 6. Motor Vehicle Manufacturers Association (Detroit)
7. Sea-Land Corporation (Edison, N.J.)
8. U.S. Immigration and Natu-

ralization Service (Washington, D.C.)

9. U.S. Department of Commerce (Washington, D.C.)

10. Embassy of Korea (Washington, D.C.)

11. World Bank (Washington, D.C.)

12. U.S. International Trade Commission (Washington, D.C.)

13. Japanese Automobile Manufacturers Association (Washington, D.C.)

14. U.S. Department of Commerce (Washington, D.C.)

15. Almond Board of California (North Highlands, Calif.)

16–18. U.S. Department of Commerce (Washington, D.C.)

19. Embassy of South Africa (Washington, D.C.)

20. Tiffany & Co. (N.Y.C.)

21, 22. Embassy of Nicaragua (Washington, D.C.)/Embassy of Japan (Washington, D.C.)

23, 24. U.S. Department of Commerce (Washington, D.C.)

25. Georgetown Economic Services (Washington, D.C.)

26. Pencil Makers Association (Marlton, N.J)

HIGH FINANCE

1. Salomon Brothers (N.Y.C.)

2. Bond Investors Association (Miami Lakes, Fla.)

3. Salomon Brothers (N.Y.C.)

4. American Council of Life Insurance (Washington, D.C.)/Bond Investors Association (Miami Lakes, Fla.)

5. IDS Financial Services (Minneapolis)

6. Federal Deposit Insurance Corporation (Washington, D.C.)

7. George Benson, Emory University (Atlanta)

8. U.S. Department of the Treasury (Washington, D.C.)

9. U.S. General Accounting Office (Washington, D.C.)/ U.S. Congressional Budget Office (Washington, D.C.)

10, 11. Edward W. Hill, Cleveland State University (Cleveland)

RESOURCES

12. U.S. Attorney General
(Washington, D.C.)
13. K. H. Thomas Associates
(Miami)
14. Resolution Trust Corporation (Washington, D.C.)
15, 16. Morgan Stanley and
Company (N.Y.C.)
17. Chrysler Corporation
(Highland Park, Mich.)
18, 19. U.S. Department of
Commerce (Washington,
D.C.)
20. Federal Reserve System
(Washington, D.C.)
21. Adams & Rinehart
(N.Y.C.)
22, 23. New York Stock Exchange (N.Y.C.)
24. Morgan Stanley and Company (N.Y.C.)
25, 26. *American Banker–Bond
Buyer* (N.Y.C.)
27, 28. Federal Bureau of Investigation (Washington,
D.C.)

CORPORATE AMERICA

1. U.S. Department of Education (Washington, D.C.)

2. Merger Statistics Review
(Schaumburg, Ill.)
3, 4. *Mergers and Acquisitions*
(Philadelphia)/U.S. Department of Justice (Washington,
D.C.)
5. Administrative Office of the
U.S. Courts (Washington,
D.C.)
6. *Fortune* (N.Y.C.)
7. U.S. Congressional Office of
Technology Assessment
(Washington, D.C.)
8. Administrative Management
Society (Trevose, Penn.)
9. *Wall Street Journal* Poll
(N.Y.C.)
10. Korn-Ferry International
(N.Y.C.)
11, 12. *A Lesser Life: The Myth
of Women's Liberation*, by
Sylvia Ann Hewlett (Wil-
liam Morrow, N.Y.C.)
13. *Wall Street Journal* Poll
(N.Y.C.)
14, 15. Hewitt Associates
(Lincolnshire, Ill.)
16. Invest-Net (North Miami,
Fla.)
17. New England Equity Institute (Cambridge, Mass.)
18, 19. United Automobile
Workers (Detroit)

20. Orsini Design Associates (N.Y.C.)
21. Recognition Equipment (Dallas)
22–25. Drexel Burnham Lambert (N.Y.C.)
26. Citizens for Tax Justice (Washington, D.C.)
27. *Barbarians at the Gate: The Fall of RJR Nabisco,* by Brian Burroughs and John Helyar (Harper & Row, N.Y.C.)
28. Heidrick & Struggles (N.Y.C.)
29. Erdos & Morgan (N.Y.C.)

10–12. U.S. Department of Labor (Washington, D.C.)
13, 14. Imberman and DeForest (Chicago)
15. National Association of Temporary Services (Alexandria, Va.)
16, 17. Center on Budget and Policy Priorities (Washington, D.C.)
18, 19. U.S. Department of Labor (Washington, D.C.)
20. Louis Harris and Associates (N.Y.C.)
21, 22. U.S. Department of Labor (Washington, D.C.)

THE LABOR FORCE

1, 2. *Forbes* (N.Y.C.)
3. U.S. Department of Labor (Washington, D.C.)
4, 5. Robert M. Costrell, University of Massachusetts (Amherst)
6. U.S. Department of Labor (Washington, D.C.)
7. The Conference Board (N.Y.C.)
8, 9. AFL-CIO (Washington, D.C.)

ON THE JOB

1. U.S. Congressional Office of Technology Assessment (Washington, D.C.)
2. Drug Policy Foundation (Washington, D.C.)
3. U.S. Department of Labor (Washington, D.C.)/*Harper's* research (N.Y.C.)
4. Runzheimer International (Rochester, Wis.)
5. International Council of Shopping Centers (N.Y.C.)/

RESOURCES

U.S. Department of Labor
(Washington, D.C.)

6. Gallup Organization
(Princeton, N.J.)

7, 8. London House (Park
Ridge, Ill.)

9. U.S. Department of Labor
(Washington, D.C.)

10. Louis Harris and Associates
(N.Y.C.)

11, 12. Roper Organization
(N.Y.C.)

13, 14. Porter-Novelli (Chicago)

15. Rhône-Poulenc Ag Company (Research Triangle
Park, N.C.)

16. New York City Department of Transportation
(N.Y.C.)

17. *The Firefighters' Cookbook*,
by John Sineno (Vintage,
N.Y.C.)

18. U.S. Bureau of the Census
(Washington, D.C.)

SHOPPING

1. International Council of
Shopping Centers (N.Y.C.)

2, 3. *Harper's* research
(N.Y.C.)

4. American Bankers Association (Washington, D.C.)

5. Tweeds (Edgewater, N.J.)

6. Wool Bureau (N.Y.C.)

7, 8. R. H. Bruskin Associates
(New Brunswick, N.J.)

9, 10. Ford Motor Company
(Dearborn, Mich.)

11. Worldwatch Institute
(Washington, D.C.)

12, 13. Produce Marketing Association (Newark, Del.)

14. Point of Purchase Advertising Institute (Fort Lee,
N.J.)

15. Robert Schindler, Rutgers
University (Camden, N.J.)

PRICE TAGS

1. Summum (Salt Lake City)
2. Bloodline (Florham Park,
N.J.)
3. Meadox Medicals (Oakland,
N.J.)
4. Hospital for Special Surgery
(N.Y.C.)

5. *U.S. News & World Report* (Washington, D.C.)
6. D. N. Shalin, Harvard University (Cambridge, Mass.)
7. Idant Labs (N.Y.C.)
8, 9. Holstein Association (Brattleboro, Vt.)
10. World Wildlife Fund (Washington, D.C.)
11. Larson Company (Tucson, Ariz.)
12. Landscape Services (Santa Barbara, Calif.)
13. North Country Corporation (Cambridge, Mass.)
14. Lobel's Prime Meats (N.Y.C.)
15. Northland Service (Seattle)
16. Mendocino Beverage Company (Vineburg, Calif.)
17. Letitia Baldridge Enterprises (Washington, D.C.)
18. Scandal Tours (Washington, D.C.)
19. Richard Nixon Library and Birthplace (Yorba Linda, Calif.)
20. Sotheby's Auction House (N.Y.C.)
21. Ross-Dove Company (Foster City, Calif.)
22. *Fortune* (N.Y.C.)

SCIENCE

TECHNOLOGY

1. National Institute for Occupational Safety and Health (Atlanta)
2. Robotics Industries Association (Ann Arbor, Mich.)
3, 4. Gary Saxonhouse, University of Michigan (Ann Arbor)
5. Joel Yudken, Association for Computing Machinery (New Brunswick, N.J.)
6. McAfee Associates (Santa Clara, Calif.)
7. Nippon Telegraph and Telephone America (N.Y.C.)
8. *Channels* (N.Y.C.)
9. Genemsco Corporation (Kingston, Mass.)
10. Department of Animal Sciences, University of California (Davis)
11, 12. U.S. Congressional Office of Technology Assessment (Washington, D.C.)
13, 14. Du Pont (Wilmington, Del.)
15. Alcor Foundation (Riverside, Calif.)

16. Reanimation Foundation (Vaduz, Liechtenstein)
17. Larry Spruch, New York University (N.Y.C.)
18. *Science News* (Washington, D.C.)
19. King Research (Chattanooga, Tenn.)
20. Velcro USA (Manchester, N.H.)
21. Sacramento Animal Medical Group (Carmichael, Calif.)
22. International Society for Heart and Lung Transplantation (San Diego)

OUTER SPACE

1–3. Gallup Organization (Princeton, N.J.)
4. International Flat Earth Research Society (Lancaster, Calif.)
5. U.S. Library of Congress (Washington, D.C.)
6. National Aeronautics and Space Administration (Houston)
7. U.S. Department of the Navy (Washington, D.C.)

8. Joseph Silk, University of California (Berkeley)
9. Tom Walker, A.P. Dow Jones (Brussels)
10. *Des Moines Register* Iowa Poll (Des Moines)
11. Campbell Communications (Bethesda, Md.)
12. U.S. Bureau of the Census (Washington, D.C.)
13, 14. Goddard Space Flight Center (Greenbelt, Md.)
15. U.S. Congressional Office of Technology Assessment (Washington, D.C.)
16. Kennedy Space Center (Fla.)
17. Marshall Space Flight Center (Huntsville, Ala.)
18. *The Houston Post* (Houston, Tex.)/*Harper's* research (N.Y.C.)
19. American Astronomical Society (Washington, D.C.)

WEATHER CONDITIONS

1. Sallie Baliunas, Harvard University Smithsonian Center for Astrophysics (Cambridge, Mass.)

RESOURCES

2. Jim Hansen and Sergej Lebedeff (N.Y.C.)
3. *Des Moines Register* Iowa Poll (Des Moines)
4. National Oceanic and Atmospheric Administration (Washington, D.C.)
5. John Miller, Northern Illinois University (De Kalb)
6. National Lightning Protection Institute (Harvard, Ill.)
7, 8. National Science Foundation (Washington, D.C.)
9. National Center for Health Statistics (Hyattsville, Md)
10, 11. National Climatic Data Center (Asheville, N.C.)
12. David A. Robinson, Rutgers University (New Brunswick, N.J.)
13. Charles Knight, National Center for Atmospheric Research (Boulder, Colo.)
14. Salt Institute (Alexandria, Va.)
15. Snow-Engineering Incorporated (Littleton, N.H.)
16. R. H. Bruskin Associates (New Brunswick, N.J.)
17. National Severe Storm Forecast Center (Kansas City, Mo.)

18. National Climatic Data Center (Asheville, N.C.)
19. *Innumeracy: Mathematical Illiteracy and Its Consequences,* by John Allen Paulos (Farrar Straus Giroux, N.Y.C.)
20. Shaw Creations (N.Y.C.)

REAPING AND SOWING

1. *Biodiversity,* by E. O. Wilson (National Academy Press, Washington, D.C.)
2. Ciba-Geigy Corporation (Greensboro, N.C.)
3. U.S. Department of Agriculture (Washington, D.C.)
4. U.S. Food and Drug Administration (Washington, D.C.)
5. U.S. Environmental Protection Agency (Washington, D.C.)
6. David Pimental, Cornell University (Ithaca, N.Y.)
7. Pesticide Action Network (San Francisco)
8. Iowa Department of Natural Resources (Iowa City)
9. U.S. Department of Agriculture (Washington, D.C.)

RESOURCES

10. U.S. General Accounting Office (Washington, D.C.)
11. The WEFA Group (Bala Cynwyd, Pa.)
12, 13. U.S. Department of Agriculture (Washington, D.C.)
14. Farm and Industrial Equipment Institute (Chicago)
15, 16. Standard Rate and Data Service (Wilmette, Ill.)
17. Worldwatch Institute (Washington, D.C.)
18. U.S. Department of Agriculture (Washington, D.C.)
19. U.S. Department of Agriculture (Washington, D.C.)/ *Harper's* research (N.Y.C.)
20. Gardens for All (Burlington, Vt.)/Gallup Organization (Princeton, N.J.)
21, 22. National Gardening Association (Burlington, Vt.)
23. World Pumpkin Confederation (Collins, N.Y.)
24. Clover Specialty Company (St. Petersburg, Fla.)
25. *Black's Veterinary Dictionary* (A & C Black, London)

THE ANIMAL KINGDOM

1. U.S. Patent Office (Washington, D.C.)
2. Foundation on Economic Trends (Washington, D.C.)
3. People for the Ethical Treatment of Animals (Bethesda, Md.)
4. Northumbria Police (South Shields, England)
5. Gates Rubber Company (Dumfries, Scotland)
6. Stevens Point City Hall (Stevens Point, Wis.)
7. Florida Alligator Association (Tallahassee, Fla.)
8. Animal Protection Institute of America (Sacramento, Calif.)
9, 10. National Wild Turkey Federation (Edgefield, S.C.)
11. U.S. Fish and Wildlife Service (Anchorage)
12, 13. Reuters (N.Y.C.)
14. Edward O. Wilson, Harvard University (Cambridge, Mass.)
15. *Microcosmos,* by Lynn Margulis and Dorion Sagan (Summit Books, N.Y.C.)
16. Smithsonian Institution (Washington, D.C.)

17. Edward O. Wilson, Harvard University (Cambridge, Mass.)
18. National Center for Atmospheric Research (Boulder, Colo.)
19. *National Geographic* (Washington, D.C.)
20. Pennsylvania Game Commission (Harrisburg, Pa.)
21. Alaska Fish and Wildlife Research Center (Anchorage)
22. Great Bear Mountain (Missoula, Mont.)
23. U.S. Fish and Wildlife Service (Laurel, Md.)
24. New York City Department of Parks and Recreation (N.Y.C.)
25. New York Botanical Garden (Bronx, N.Y.)
26, 27. Rich Blohm (Huntington, N.Y.)
28, 29. George P. Georgehiou, University of California (Riverside)
30. Edward O. Wilson, Harvard University (Cambridge, Mass.)
31, 32. American Museum of Natural History (N.Y.C.)

THE ENVIRONMENT

1. United Nations Environment Program (N.Y.C.)
2. World Environment Center (N.Y.C.)
3. Gallup Organization (Princeton, N.J.)
4, 5. National Park Service (Washington, D.C.)
6. National Audubon Society (Olympia, Wash.)
7. U.S. Forest Service (Washington, D.C.)
8. Harper & Row (San Francisco)
9. World Resources Institute (Washington, D.C.)
10. U.S. Environmental Protection Agency (Washington, D.C.)
11. Citizens' Clearinghouse for Hazardous Wastes (Arlington, Va.)
12. Port Authority of New York and New Jersey (N.Y.C.)
13. Society of the Plastics Industry (Washington, D.C.)
14–16. U.S. Environmental Protection Agency (Washington, D.C.)

RESOURCES

17. Environmental Action Foundation (Washington, D.C.)
18. U.S. Environmental Protection Agency (Washington, D.C.)
19. Natural Resources Defense Council (Washington, D.C.)
20. U.S. Environmental Protection Agency (Washington, D.C.)
21. Nuclear Information and Resource Service (Washington, D.C.)
22. U.S. Department of Defense (Washington, D.C.)/ U.S. Environmental Protection Agency (Washington, D.C.)
23. U.S. Environmental Protection Agency (Washington, D.C.)
24. U.S. Congressional Office of Technology Assessment (Washington, D.C.)
25. Greenpeace (Washington, D.C.)
26. New York State Department of Environmental Conservation (Albany)
27. National Oceanic and Atmospheric Administration (Silver Spring, Md.)

28. Barry Commoner, Center for the Biology of Natural Systems, Queens College, City University of New York (Queens, N.Y.)
29, 30. U.S. Agency for International Development (Washington, D.C.)
31. Worldwatch Institute (Washington, D.C.)
32. U.S. Environmental Protection Agency (Washington, D.C.)
33. United Nations Environmental Program (Geneva)
34, 35. Sierra Club (Washington, D.C.)
36. Mount Everest International Peace Climb (Port Townsend, Wash.)
37. New York City Department of Parks and Recreation (N.Y.C.)

ENERGY

1. U.S. Nuclear Regulatory Commission (Washington, D.C.)

2. Public Citizen (Washington, D.C.)

3. Roper Organization (N.Y.C.)

4. Byelorussian Mission to the United Nations (N.Y.C.)

5–8. U.S. Department of Energy (Washington, D.C.)

9. U.S. Library of Congress (Washington, D.C.)

10, 11. Solar Energy Industries Association (Washington, D.C.)

12. American Business Information (Omaha)

13. Greenpeace (Washington, D.C.)

14. Michael Oppenheimer, Environmental Defense Fund (N.Y.C.)

15. Earthscan (Washington, D.C.)

16. U.S. Department of Energy (Washington, D.C.)

17. U.S. Department of Transportation (Washington, D.C.)

18. Bill Slate, *Newsweek* (N.Y.C.)

19. Tank Automotive Command, U.S. Department of the Army (Warren, Mich.)

20. U.S. Environmental Protection Agency (Washington, D.C.)

21. Safe Energy Communication Council (Washington, D.C.)

22. U.S. Department of Energy (Washington, D.C.)

23. A. H. Rosenfeld, University of California (Berkeley)

24. U.S. Department of Energy (Washington, D.C.)

25. Peter Vitousek, Ann Ehrlich, and Paul Ehrlich, Stanford University (Palo Alto, Calif.)

26. *Living Fishes of the World,* by Earl Stannard Herald (Doubleday, N.Y.C.)

27. *Perspectives in Biology and Medicine,* by Horton A. Johnson (University of Chicago Press, Chicago)

28. IBM (Armonk, N.Y.)

29. Louis Sokoloff, National Institute of Mental Health (Bethesda, Md.)/M&M Mars (Hackettstown, N.J.)

30. Peter R. Friedman, Kessler and Kemper (N.Y.C.)

RESOURCES

HEALTH RISKS

1, 2. U.S. Environmental Protection Agency (Washington, D.C.)

3. Centers for Disease Control (Atlanta)

4. Distilled Spirits Council of the U.S. (Washington, D.C.)

5. Alcohol Research Information Services (Lansing, Mich.)

6. U.S. Congressional Office of Technology Assessment (Washington, D.C.)

7. American Academy of Allergy and Immunology (Milwaukee)

8–11. American Cancer Society (N.Y.C.)

12. Gallup Organization (Princeton, N.J.)

13. Alan Guttmacher Institute (N.Y.C.)

14. National Institute of Environmental Health Sciences (Washington, D.C.)

15. New York City Department of Health (N.Y.C.)

16, 17. San Francisco Sexually Transmitted Disease Control Clinic (San Francisco)

18. National Institute of Mental Health (Bethesda, Md.)

19, 20. National Center for Health Statistics (Hyattsville, Md.)

21. Julia Child (Cambridge, Mass.)

HEALTH CARE

1. U.S. Bureau of the Census (Washington, D.C.)

2. U.S. Health Care Financing Administration (Baltimore)

3–5. U.S. Department of Health and Human Services (Washington, D.C.)

6. Society for the Right to Die (N.Y.C.)

7. U.S. Bureau of the Census (Washington, D.C.)

8. Education Council for Foreign Medical Graduates (Philadelphia, Pa.)

9–11. Association of American Medical Colleges (Washington, D.C.)

12. American College of Obstetricians and Gynecologists (Washington, D.C.)

13. American Medical Association (Chicago)
14, 15. Norbert Gleisher, Mt. Sinai Hospital (Chicago)
16. Alan Guttmacher Institute (N.Y.C.)
17. National Center for Health Statistics (Hyattsville, Md.)
18. Sarah Shuptrine and Associates (Columbia, S.C.)
19, 20. Alan Sager, Boston University (Boston)
21, 22. Physicians for Social Responsibility (Washington, D.C.)
23. Surfer's Medical Association (San Francisco)
24. American Cancer Society (N.Y.C.)
25. National Center for Health Statistics (Hyattsville, Md.)
26. Union of American Physicians and Dentists (Oakland, Calif.)
27. Federation of State Medical Boards of the United States (Fort Worth)
28. *Journal of the American Medical Association* (Chicago)
29. Norman Farnsworth, University of Illinois (Chicago)
30. Leeches USA (Westbury, N.Y.)
31, 32. Porter-Novelli (Chicago)
33. American Dental Hygienists' Association (Chicago)

THE AIDS VIRUS

1, 2. World Health Organization (Geneva)
3. Centers for Disease Control (Atlanta)
4. National Center for Health Statistics (Hyattsville, Md.)
5. *Los Angeles Times* Poll (Los Angeles)
6. World Health Organization (Geneva)
7. Centers for Disease Control (Atlanta)/*Harper's* research (N.Y.C.)
8, 9. National Student Nurses Association (N.Y.C.)
10. U.S. House of Representatives Subcommittee on Health and Long-Term Care (Washington, D.C.)
11. New York City Mayor's Commission on the Future of Child Health (N.Y.C.)
12. New York City Department of Health (N.Y.C.)

13. Sero-Prevalence Unit (N.Y.C.)
14. New York City Blood Center (N.Y.C.)
15. *New York Times* Poll (N.Y.C.)
16. *Los Angeles Times* Poll (Los Angeles)
17. Illinois Department of Public Health (Springfield, Ill.)

PSYCHOLOGY

ANXIETY

1, 2. American Psychiatric Association (Washington, D.C.)
3. New York City Transit Authority (N.Y.C.)
4, 5. U.S. National Institute for Occupational Safety and Health (Washington, D.C.)
6. John Robinson, University of Maryland (College Park)
7. *Medical World News* (Houston)
8. Ramsey Dry Eye and Tear Research Center (St. Paul)

9. Kepner-Tregoe (Princeton, N.J.)
10. *The Teenage World,* by Daniel Offer (Plenum, N.Y.C.)
11. Field Publications (Middletown, Conn.)
12. Trinity School (N.Y.C.)
13. Stanford University (Stanford, Calif.)
14. T. D. Borkovec, Pennsylvania State University (University Park)
15. *The Teenage World,* by Daniel Offer (Plenum, N.Y.C.)

NARCISSISM

1. D'Arcy Masius Benton & Bowles (N.Y.C.)
2. American Society of Plastic and Reconstructive Surgeons (Arlington Heights, Ill.)
3. American Academy of Cosmetic Surgery (Newport Beach, Calif.)
4. American Society of Plastic and Reconstructive Surgeons (Arlington Heights, Ill.)/ Gerald Pitman (N.Y.C.)/

RESOURCES

Collagen Corporation (Palo Alto, Calif.)/Dow Corning (Midland, Mich.)/*Harper's* research (N.Y.C.)

5, 6. Maidenform (N.Y.C.)

7. Brian Novack (Beverly Hills, Calif.)

8. La Carezza (N.Y.C.)

9. *Innumeracy: Mathematical Illiteracy and Its Consequences,* by John Allen Paulos (Farrar Straus Giroux, N.Y.C.)

10. *Gentlemen's Quarterly* (N.Y.C.)

11. Scholl, Incorporated (Memphis)

12. Combe (White Plains, N.Y.)

13, 14. Dr. Scholl's Poll by the Gallup Organization (Princeton, N.J.)

15. William A. Rossi (Marshfield, Mass.)

16, 17. Richard Rubenstein Agency (N.Y.C.)

18. MRCA Information Services (Northbrook, Ill.)

19, 20. National Center for Health Statistics (Hyattsville, Md.)

21. Mattel (Los Angeles)

22, 23. *Singles: The New Americans,* by Jacqueline Simenauer and David Carroll (Simon & Schuster, N.Y.C.)

24. Stanley H. Biber (Trinidad, Colo.)

25. Mayo Clinic (Scottsdale, Ariz.)

26. Cadwell Davis Partners (N.Y.C.)

27. *Des Moines Register* Iowa Poll (Des Moines)

28. The Humor Project (Saratoga Springs, N.Y.)

29. Roper Organization (N.Y.C.)

30. Frank Dumont (Atlantic City)

31. Skin Cancer Foundation (N.Y.C.)

32. Yellow Pages Research Group (Omaha)

33, 34. MRCA Information Services (Stamford, Conn.)

35. *Diana's Diary: An Intimate Portrait of the Princess of Wales,* by Andrew Morton (Summit, N.Y.C.)

36. Giuliano Ferrieri, *Europeo* (Milan)

37. PrimaDonna Beauty Care Center (Brooklyn, N.Y.)

38. Gillette (Boston)

RESOURCES

FEARS

1. National Institute of Mental Health (Rockville, Md.)
2. Karen Glenn, Scholastic, Incorporated (N.Y.C.)
3. National Safe Kids Campaign (Washington, D.C.)
4. Center for Media and Public Affairs (Washington, D.C.)
5, 6. Jensen Communications (Burbank, Calif.)
7. Christie Brinkley (N.Y.C.)
8, 9. Americans Talk Security (Winchester, Mass.)
10. DOOM, the Society for Secular Armageddonism (San Francisco)
11. Waldenbooks (Stamford, Conn.)
12. Defense Budget Project (Washington, D.C.)/National Security Archives (Washington, D.C.)
13. The Spy Connection (Hawthorne, Calif.)
14. Tom Zizzo (N.Y.C.)
15, 16. Media General (Richmond, Va.)–Associated Press (N.Y.C.) Poll
17. Hall Crest Systems (McLean, Va.)

18. Lucy Hughes-Hallet, *The Sunday Telegraph* (London)
19. Warren Jones, University of Tennessee (Knoxville)
20. Oxtoby-Smith (N.Y.C.)
21. U.S. Air Fearful Flyers Program (Pittsburgh)
22. Western Insurance Information Service (Los Angeles)
23. National Safety Council (Chicago)
24. *Public Opinion* Poll by Louis Harris and Associates (N.Y.C.)
25, 26. National Safety Council (Chicago)

BELIEFS

1. Christian Broadcast Center (Richmond, Va.)/Gallup Organization (Princeton, N.J.)
2. Gallup Organization (Princeton, N.J.)
3. Notre Dame University (Notre Dame, Ind.)
4. John Miller, Northern Illinois University (De Kalb)
5. Gallup Organization (Princeton, N.J.)

6. Kenneth Woodward, *News-week* (N.Y.C.)
7. *A Secret World,* by A. W. Richard Sipe (Brunner Mazel, N.Y.C.)
8. Alan Guttmacher Institute (N.Y.C.)
9, 10. Gallup Organization (Princeton, N.J.)
11. Church of Jesus Christ of Latter-Day Saints (Salt Lake City)
12. The Referral Service (Santa Fe)
13. Gallup Organization (Princeton, N.J.)
14. Bishopric of the Russian Orthodox Church (N.Y.C.)
15. Yair Bar-El (Jerusalem)
16. Oxford University Centre for Postgraduate Hebrew Studies (Oxford, England)
17. Alicia Patterson Foundation (Bethesda, Md.)
18. Vicaría de la Solidaridad (Santiago, Chile)
19. Catholic Traditionalist Movement (Westbury, Conn.)
20. Gospel Music Association (Nashville)
21. Gallup Organization (Princeton, N.J.)

22. Stephen Wizenburg, Grand View College (Des Moines)
23. U.S. Internal Revenue Service (Washington, D.C.)
24. *Freedom Writer Newsletter* (Great Barrington, Mass.)
25. Gallup Organization (Princeton, N.J.)
26. Laurie Cabot (Salem, Mass.)
27. American Federation of Astrologers (Tempe, Ariz.)
28. American Astronomical Society (Washington, D.C.)
29. Gallup Organization (Princeton, N.J.)
30. Christian Motorcyclists Association (Hatfield, Ark.)
31. Embassy of Japan (Washington, D.C.)
32, 33. Cathedral of St. John the Divine (N.Y.C.)

HOME EC

MARRIED LIFE

1. National Center for Health Statistics (Hyattsville, Md.)

RESOURCES

2. Metropolitan Life Insurance Company (N.Y.C.)

3, 4. Korbel Champagne Cellars (Guerneville, Calif.) Poll by R. H. Bruskin Associates (New Brunswick, N.J.)

5. *Bride's Magazine* (N.Y.C.)/U.S. Bureau of the Census (Washington, D.C.)

6. Goldfield Mineral Services (London)

7. *Harper's* research (N.Y.C.)

8. *Washington Report* (St. Petersburg, Fla.)

9, 10. *Time* (N.Y.C.)

11. Where's the ART!!, a Gallery of Art for the Smart (Portland, Ore.)

12. Larry Bumpass, University of Wisconsin (Madison)

13. U.S. Bureau of the Census (Washington, D.C.)

14, 15. Neil G. Bennett and Patricia Craig, Yale University (New Haven), and David E. Bloom, Columbia University (N.Y.C.)

16, 17. U.S. Bureau of the Census (Washington, D.C.)

18, 19. National Opinion Research Center (Chicago)

20. Gallup Organization (Princeton, N.J.)

21, 22. *Adultery: An Analysis of Love and Betrayal,* by Annette Lawson (Basic Books, N.Y.C.)

23. Danish Ministry of Justice (Copenhagen)

24, 25. National Bureau of Economic Research (Cambridge, Mass.)

26, 27. *Chicago Sun-Times* (Chicago)

28–30. National Center for Health Statistics (Hyattsville, Md.)

31, 32. *USA Today* Poll (Arlington, Va.)

33, 34. *Rape and Marriage,* by Diana Russell (Indiana University Press, Bloomington, Ind.)

35. U.S. Department of Justice (Washington, D.C.)

36. Lawyers Collective (Bombay, India)

37. Bridgeport Police Department (Bridgeport, Conn.)

MODERN BABY MAKING

1. American Fertility Society (Birmingham, Ala.)

RESOURCES

2, 3. National Association of Surrogate Mothers (Beverly Hills, Calif.)

4–6. U.S. Congressional Office of Technology Assessment (Washington, D.C.)

7, 8. Alan Guttmacher Institute (N.Y.C.)

9. Research and Forecast (N.Y.C.)

10, 11. Alan Guttmacher Institute (N.Y.C.)

12, 13. *American Baby* (N.Y.C.)

14. Alan Guttmacher Institute (N.Y.C.)

15. U.S. Department of Commerce (Washington, D.C.)/ U.S. Department of Health and Human Services (Washington, D.C.)

16. National Center for Health Statistics (Hyattsville, Md.)

17. Daniel Seiver, Miami University (Oxford, Ohio)

18. U.S. Bureau of the Census (Washington, D.C.)

19, 20. No-Circ (San Anselmo, Calif.)

21. Goldson Associates (Washington, D.C.)

22. U.S. Bureau of the Census (Washington, D.C.)

23. Carl Lehrburger (Sheffield, Mass.)

24. Institute for the Achievement of Human Potential (Philadelphia)

25. Creative Programming (N.Y.C.)

FAMILY AFFAIRS

1. U.S. Department of Labor (Washington, D.C.)

2, 3. U.S. Bureau of the Census (Washington, D.C.)

4. *Mothers on Trial,* by Phyllis Chesler (McGraw-Hill, N.Y.C.)

5. National Center for Missing and Exploited Children (Washington, D.C.)

6, 7. Sex Information and Education Council of the United States (N.Y.C.)

8, 9. *Parenting* (San Francisco)

10. U.S. Department of Education (Washington, D.C.)

11. *USA Today* Poll (Arlington, Va.)

12. Fortino and Associates (Pittsburgh)

RESOURCES

13–16. U.S. Bureau of the Census (Washington, D.C.)

17. Child Trends (Washington, D.C.)

18, 19. Barbara Carson, Ball State University (Muncie, Ind.)

20. Market Facts (Washington, D.C.)

21. Roper Organization (N.Y.C.)

22. National Center for Health Statistics (Hyattsville, Md.)

23. U.S. Bureau of the Census (Washington, D.C.)

24. Hallmark Cards (Kansas City, Mo.)

AROUND THE HOUSE

1. Paul Lachance, Rutgers University (New Brunswick, N.J.)

2. Association of Home Appliance Manufacturers (Chicago)

3. Packaged Facts (N.Y.C.)

4. *Better Homes and Gardens* (Des Moines)

5. Saran Wrap Poll by the Gallup Organization (Princeton, N.J.)

6. S. C. Johnson & Son, Inc. (Racine, Wis.)

7. Roper Organization (N.Y.C.)

8, 9. Across the Board (N.Y.C.)

10, 11. National Gardening Association (Burlington, Vt.)

12. O. M. Scott and Sons (Marysville, Ohio)/National Gardening Association (Burlington, Vt.)

13. Simmons Market Research (N.Y.C.)

14. John L. Stanton, St. Joseph's University (Philadelphia)

15. MRCA Information Services (Northbrook, Ill.)

16, 17. Robert Organization (N.Y.C.)

18. Stanford University Sleep Disorder Clinic (Stanford, Calif.)

19. U.S. Bureau of the Census (Washington, D.C.)

20, 21. R. H. Bruskin Associates (New Brunswick, N.J.)

22. Procter & Gamble (Cincinnati)

23, 24. *Des Moines Register* Iowa Poll (Des Moines)
25. Eagle Forum (Alton, Ill.)
26. Cyberworks (Orillia, Ontario)
27. LINK Resources (N.Y.C.)
28. U.S. Consumer Product Safety Commission (Bethesda, Md.)
29. U.S. Consumer Product Safety Commission (Washington, D.C.)
30. Spiegel Incorporated (Chicago)

EDIBLES AND POTABLES

1. National Restaurant Association (Washington, D.C.)
2, 3. National Pasta Association (Arlington, Va.)
4. Realeat Company Poll by the Gallup Organization (London)
5, 6. U.S. Department of Agriculture (Washington, D.C.)
7. Hormel Company (Austin, Minn.)
8–10. U.S. Department of Agriculture (Washington, D.C.)
11. U.S. Department of Labor (Washington, D.C.)
12. U.S. Department of Agriculture (Washington, D.C.)
13. U.S. Food and Drug Administration (Washington, D.C.)
14, 15. U.S. Department of Agriculture (Washington, D.C.)
16, 17. Impact Databank (London)
18. Harry M. Stevens (Louisville, Ky.)
19. Tea Council of the United States (N.Y.C.)
20, 21. National Coffee Association of America (N.Y.C.)
22. SAMI (N.Y.C.)
23. Roper Organization (N.Y.C.)
24. Arthur Foods, Dodger Stadium (Los Angeles)
25. Le Bernardin (N.Y.C.)
26. Monterey Bay Aquarium (Monterey, Calif.)
27. Bryan Miller (N.Y.C.)
28. Cornell University School of Hotel Administration (Ithaca, N.Y.)
29. Roper Organization (N.Y.C.)

30. Centre Jean Rostand (Pouydesseaux, France)
31, 32. Town & Country Catering (London)
33. Kellogg Company (Battle Creek, Mich.)
34. SAMI (N.Y.C.)
35. U.S. Human Nutrition Information Service (Hyattsville, Md.)
36. Ben & Jerry's (Waterbury, Vt.)
37. Calorie Control Council (Atlanta)
38. *Gorman's New Product News* (Chicago)
39. American Institute of Baking (Manhattan, Kan.)
40. Lender's Bagel Bakery (West Haven, Conn.)
41. Pickle Packers International (St. Charles, Ill.)

SHELTER

1. National Association of Home Builders (Washington, D.C.)
2. U.S. Bureau of the Census (Washington, D.C.)
3. Coalition for the Homeless (N.Y.C.)
4. Community Service Society of New York (N.Y.C.)
5. Richard Marisco, New York Law School (N.Y.C.)
6. New York City Human Resources Administration (N.Y.C.)
7, 8. National Coalition Against Domestic Violence (Washington, D.C.)
9. National Bureau of Economic Research (Cambridge, Mass.)
10. U.S. Office of Management and Budget (Washington, D.C.)
11. U.S. Department of Housing and Urban Development (Washington, D.C.)
12. Citizens for Tax Justice (Washington, D.C.)
13. New York City Housing Authority (N.Y.C.)
14. Coalition for the Homeless (N.Y.C.)
15. Bide-a-Wee Home Association (N.Y.C.)

16. Pat Shield, *The Record* (Hackensack, N.J.)
17. Bat Conservation International (Austin, Tex.)
18. Cairo Office of City Planning (Cairo)
19. Middle East Watch (N.Y.C.)
20. U.S. Bureau of the Census (Washington, D.C.)/Greenwich Board of Realtors (Greenwich, Conn.)
21, 22. National Association of Realtors (Chicago)
23. D. F. Sly and Muhammed Bailey, Florida State University (Tallahassee, Fla.)
24. Federal Emergency Management Agency (Washington, D.C.)
25. Revitalization Agency (Niagara Falls, N.Y.)
26, 27. Mortgage Bankers Association of America (Washington, D.C.)
28. Chicago Title Insurance Company (Chicago)
29. Jules's Undersea Lodge (Key Largo, Fla.)
30. Taj Mahal (Atlantic City)
31. Rolfe City Hall (Rolfe, Iowa)

PETS

1. U.S. Bureau of the Census (Washington, D.C.)/ Humane Society of the United States (Washington, D.C.)
2. Stephen Holzman, Nassau-Suffolk Veterinary Hospital (Farmingdale, N.Y.)
3. Ruffco Enterprises (Peekskill, N.Y.)
4. Zoology Institute, University of Zurich (Zurich)
5. W. O. Whitney (Houston)
6. Robert Demling, Brigham and Women's Hospital (Boston)
7. Humane Society of the United States (Washington, D.C.)
8. Portman Veterinary Clinic (London)
9. *Texas Monthly* (Austin, Tex.)
10. Pet Rest (Lima, Ohio)
11. International Pet Cemetery Association (South Bend, Ind.)
12. Delta Society (Renton, Wash.)
13. Alpo Pet Food (Allentown, Pa.)

14, 15. A. C. Nielsen Media Research (Chicago)

16. Gallup Organization (Princeton, N.J.)/Pet Industry Joint Advisory Council (Washington, D.C.)

17. Center for Interaction of Animals and Society, University of Pennsylvania (Philadelphia)

18, 19. Village Dawg Shoppe (Rockville Centre, N.Y.)

20. Creative Programming (N.Y.C.)

21. Illinois Animal Poison Information Center (Chicago)

22. World Wildlife Fund (Washington, D.C.)

23. *Ostrich News* (Cache, Okla.)

24. *Des Moines Register* Iowa Poll (Des Moines)

VACATION

HOLIDAYS

1. Hallmark Cards (Kansas City, Mo.)

2. National Christmas Tree Association (Milwaukee)

3. American Jewish Committee (N.Y.C.)

4. U.S. Geological Survey (Reston, Va.)

5. *In Health* (Sausalito, Calif.)

6. Irving Berlin Music Company (N.Y.C.)

7. New York City Ballet (N.Y.C.)

8. Lobel's Prime Meats (N.Y.C.)

9–11. Provident National Bank (Philadelphia)

12. Roper Organization (N.Y.C.)

13. Ogilvy and Mather (N.Y.C.)

14. Greeting Card Association (Washington, D.C.)

15–17. Hallmark Cards (Kansas City, Mo.)

18. American Telephone and Telegraph Company (Basking Ridge, N.J.)

19. National Restaurant Association (Washington, D.C.)

20. Weight Watchers International (Jericho, N.Y.)

21, 22. National Turkey Federation (Reston, Va.)

23. American Academy of Cosmetic Surgery (Arcadia, Calif.)

TRAVEL AND TOURISM

1. Pan American Airlines (N.Y.C.)
2. Air Transport Association of America (Washington, D.C.)
3. *Frequent Newsletter* (Colorado Springs)
4. *Harper's* research (N.Y.C.)
5. Cunard Lines (N.Y.C.)
6. Adventure Network International (Vancouver, British Columbia)
7. National Science Foundation (Washington, D.C.)
8. U.S. National Park Service (Washington, D.C.)/*Harper's* research (N.Y.C.)
9. City of Houston Office of Planning and Development (Houston)
10. U.S. National Park Service (Washington, D.C.)
11. U.S. Department of Transportation (Washington, D.C.)/Aircraft Owners and Pilots Association (Frederick,

Md.)/*Harper's* research (N.Y.C.)
12, 13. *Survey of American Habits,* by Mel Poretz and Barry Sinrod (Price Stern Sloan, Los Angeles)
14. *Des Moines Register* Iowa Poll (Des Moines)

THE SPORTING LIFE

1. Commissioner of Baseball (N.Y.C.)/Scoreboard (Cherry Hill, N.J.)
2, 3. Los Angeles Dodgers (Vero Beach, Fla.)
4. National Association of Professional Baseball Leagues (St. Petersburg, Fla.)
5, 6. Nexis (N.Y.C.)
7. *Sports Illustrated* (N.Y.C.)
8. Chicago Bulls (Chicago)/ Douglas Kirkpatrick (Colorado Springs)
9. Gerald Eskenazi, *The New York Times* (N.Y.C.)
10. *The Journal of Labor Economics* (Urbana, Ill.)
11. Philadelphia 76ers (Philadelphia)

12. Pacific Trading Cards (Edmonds, Wash.)
13. *Sports Collectors Digest* (Iola, Wis.)
14. Rawlings Sporting Goods Company (St. Louis)/Haitian Mission (N.Y.C.)
15. Rawlings Sporting Goods Company (St. Louis)
16. Hillerich and Bradsby (Louisville, Ky.)
17. Rawlings Sporting Goods Company (St. Louis)
18. Burns Bintliff (Millsboro, Del.)
19. Rawlings Sporting Goods Company (St. Louis)
20. *SportScience*, by Peter J. Brancazio (Simon and Schuster, N.Y.C.)
21. National Baseball Library (Cooperstown, N.Y.)
22, 23. *Baseballistics*, by Bert Randolph Sugar (St. Martin's Press, N.Y.C.)
24. Miller Brewing Company (Milwaukee)
25. New York City Director of Stadiums (Queens, N.Y.)
26. U.S. Automobile Club (Indianapolis)
27. *Harper's* research (N.Y.C.)/ *Daily News* (N.Y.C.)

28. National Hockey League (Montreal)
29, 30. Athletics Congress (Indianapolis)
31. Guinness Publishing (London)
32. *American Window Cleaner* (El Sobrante, Calif.)

THE GREAT OUTDOORS

1. U.S. Environmental Protection Agency (Research Triangle Park, N.C.)
2. American Sports Data (Hartsdale, N.Y.)/Sporting Goods Manufacturers Association (North Palm Beach, Fla.)
3. Kenzo Sato, University of Iowa (Iowa City)
4. Centers for Disease Control (Atlanta)
5, 6. U.S. Croquet Association (Palm Beach Gardens, Fla.)
7. Sporting Goods Manufacturers Association (North Palm Beach, Fla.)
8. International Cheerleading Foundation (Overland Park, Kan.)

9. California Surf Lifesaving Association (Huntington Beach, Calif.)
10. Florida Museum of Natural History (Gainesville, Fla.)
11. Dolphins Plus (Key Largo, Fla.)
12. Gallup Organization (Princeton, N.J.)
13, 14. Roper Organization (N.Y.C.)
15. St. Pierre Manufacturing (Worcester, Mass.)
16. The White House (Washington, D.C.)
17. National Golf Foundation (Jupiter, Fla.)
18. *Golf Digest* (Bridgeport, Conn.)
19. American Greyhound Track Operators Association (North Miami, Fla.)
20. Humane Society of the United States (Washington, D.C.)
21. U.S. General Accounting Office (Washington, D.C.)
22. McChord Air Force Base (Tacoma, Wash.)
23. Ben Collier (Montgomery, Ala.)
24. Georgia Department of Health and Human Services (Atlanta)
25. Humane Society of the United States (Washington, D.C.)
26. Montana State Department of Fish, Wildlife and Parks (Helena, Mont.)
27. Vermont State Department of Fish and Wildlife (Waterbury, Vt.)
28. Legislative Hotline (Madison, Wis.)

LEISURE TIME

1. University of Maryland Survey Research Center (College Park)
2. Franciscan Children's Hospital (Boston)
3. Safe Care Products (Dundee, Ill.)
4. Nintendo of America (Redmond, Wash.)
5. National Bowling Council (Washington, D.C.)
6. Manhattan Chess Club School (N.Y.C.)
7. *Guinness Book of World Records,* edited by David A. Boehm (Facts on File, N.Y.C.)
8. *Games* (N.Y.C.)

9. Butterfly World (Coconut Creek, Fla.)
10. Solair (Southbridge, Mass.)
11. Shearing-Plough (Liberty Corner, N.J.)/*Drug Store News* (N.Y.C.)
12, 13. National Spa and Pool Institute (Alexandria, Va.)
14. Outdoor Power Equipment Institute (Arlington, Va.)
15, 16. Barbecue Industry Association (Naperville, Ill.)
17. The HUMOR Project (Saratoga Springs, N.Y.)
18. Allan Hobson, Harvard Medical School (Cambridge, Mass.)
19. Ernest Hartmann, Tufts Medical School (Medford, Mass.)
20. Decision Research Council (Lexington, Mass.)

JUNK FOOD

1. M&M Mars (Hackettstown, N.J.)
2. National Institute of Dental Research (Bethesda, Md.)
3. Frito-Lay (Longwood, Fla.)
4. *Snack Food* (Duluth, Minn.)

5. Hattal-Taylor VFW Post #333 (Roxborough, Pa.)
6. *Beverage Digest* (Stamford, Conn.)
7. McCann-Erickson (N.Y.C.)
8. The Coca-Cola Company (Atlanta)
9. Continental Baking Company (St. Louis)
10, 11. International Association of Ice Cream Manufacturers (Washington, D.C.)
12. Calorie Control Center (Atlanta)
13. National Center for Health Statistics (Hyattsville, Md.)
14. The Coca-Cola Company (Atlanta)
15. *Snack Food* (Duluth, Minn.)
16. Frito-Lay (Plano, Tex.)
17. U.S. Department of Agriculture (Washington, D.C.)
18. Burger King (Miami)
19. McDonald's (Oak Brook, Ill.)
20. McDonald's of Canada (Toronto)
21. Institute for Work and Learning (Washington, D.C.)
22. National Association of Pizza Operators (Santa Claus, Ind.)

23. Jericho Promotions (N.Y.C.)
24. Domino's Pizza (Ann Arbor, Mich.)
25. Consumer Product Safety Commission (Bethesda, Md.)

SEX

1–3. *Money* (N.Y.C.)
4. National Opinion Research Center (Chicago)
5. Women Against Pornography (N.Y.C.)
6. U.S. Department of Justice (Washington, D.C.)
7, 8. *Playboy* (N.Y.C.)
9. Adult Video Association (Los Angeles)
10. U.S. Department of Health and Human Services (Washington, D.C.)
11. Planned Parenthood Federation of America (N.Y.C.)
12. Louis Harris and Associates (N.Y.C.)
13. Carter-Wallace (N.Y.C.)
14. Schmidt Laboratory Products (Little Falls, N.J.)
15, 16. Family Health International (Research Triangle Park, N.C.)/Bureau of the Census (Washington, D.C.)
17. *Time* (N.Y.C.)
18, 19. *One Medicine: A Tribute to Kurt Benirschke*, edited by O. A. Ryder and M. L. Byrd (Springer-Verlag, Berlin)
20, 21. Kinsey Institute (Bloomington, Ind.)
22, 23. *Sex, Nutrition and You*, by Gordon Tessler (Better Health, San Diego)
24. Roger W. Libby, National Organization of Sexual Enthusiasts (Atlanta)
25. Korbel Champagne Cellars (Guerneville, Calif.)
26. National Organization of Sexual Enthusiasts (Atlanta)
27. Yerkes Regional Primate Center (Atlanta)
28. Karen Killmar, San Diego Zoo (San Diego)
29. United Kingdom Department of Transportation (London)
30, 31. National Zoological Park (Washington, D.C.)
32. *Glamour* (N.Y.C.)
33, 34. Jennifer Jones, State University of New York (Albany)

RESOURCES

35. Masters & Johnson (St. Louis, Mo.)
36. City Lites (St. Petersburg, Fla.)
37. National Family Opinion Research (Toledo, Ohio)
38. Water Bed Manufacturers Association (Los Angeles)
39. *Maclean's* (Toronto)
40. *Elle* (Paris)
41. *Harper's* research (N.Y.C.)
42. *Redbook* (N.Y.C.)
43, 44. *Runner's World* (Emmaus, Pa.)
45. *Dieter's Guide to Weight Loss During Sex,* by Richard Smith (Workman, N.Y.C.)
46. Hershey Chocolate (Hershey, Pa.)

Index

INDEX

INDEX

INDEX

INDEX

INDEX

INDEX

INDEX

Hugs, 97
Human-rights abuses, 73, 74
Humidity, 137
Humming, 100
Hummingbirds, 142
Humor, 15, 32, 46, 162
101 Dalmations, 98
Hunting, 198–99
Hussein, Saddam, 47

Iacocca, Lee, 123
IBM, 116, 148
Ice, 130, 138, 148, 182
Icebergs, 130
Ice cream, 15, 88, 183, 202
Iceland, 21
I Gotta Be Me, 104
Illegal aliens, 81
Illinois, 155, 188
Illness, 126–27
"I'll Take Manhattan," 86
Immigration and Naturalization Service (INS), 81
Imports, 116–18
Inaugurations, 72
Income, 9, 13, 23, 31, 38, 51, 73, 79, 98, 101, 112, 113, 114, 122–23, 124, 139, 140, 180, 184, 185, 194
Indecent gestures, 84

Independence movements, 56
India, 56, 70, 118, 173
Indiana Jones and the Last Crusade, 98
Indianapolis 500, 196
Infant mortality, 112
Inflation, 124
Information operators, 107
Inheritance, 112
Injuries, 38, 60, 108, 165, 180, 197, 198
Innuendos, 97
Insecticide, 139, 142
Insects, 25, 141–43
Insolvencies, 119–20, 122, 123
Insurance, 119, 139, 150–51, 152, 165
Interest, 78, 116
Internal Revenue Service (IRS), 28, 114, 167
International Flat Earth Research Society, 135
International Monetary Fund (IMF), 116
Interracial marriage, 36, 37
Intersex, 56
Invasions, 70, 71, 73
Iowa, 42, 43, 76, 83, 89, 100, 101, 102, 136, 137, 139, 140, 162, 180, 188, 194

Iran, 130
Iran-Contra scandal, 16, 52
Iran–Iraq War, 63, 76
Iraq, 59, 76, 148, 164
Israel, 37, 75–76, 77, 108, 181, 185
Italy, 181
Ivy League, 16

Jackson, Jesse, 10
Jagger, Mick, 65, 101
Jails, 22, 23
January, 171
Japan, 3, 5, 78–80, 116, 117, 118, 121, 133, 160, 168, 204
Japanese language, 80
Jazz, 102
Jeeps, 42
Jelly beans, 53
Jenne, Steve, 65
Jeremy's Place, 38
Jerusalem, 166
Jet, 35
Jews, 76, 81, 97, 166, 191
Jobs, 111, 122, 124, 126–27, 133, 202
Jogging trails, 84
Johnson, Ross, 123
Jokes, 15, 32, 46
Joplin, Janis, 101
Jordan, Michael, 195
Journalists, 52, 93, 95
Judges, 16, 33

INDEX

INDEX

INDEX

Mortgages, 184, 185

Moscow, 55, 56, 90, 129, 202

Mosques, 76

Motherfucker, 102

Mothers, 37, 174, 175, 176–77. *See also* Parents

Mother's Day, 192

Motion sickness, 135

Mount Everest, 146

Movies, 13, 14, 86, 98–100

Movie theaters, 98, 206

Mowing lawns, 165, 200

M16 rifle, 62

Mud, 195

Mugabe, Robert, 22

Mules, 60, 107

Mummification, 129

Murder, 20, 23, 33, 37, 40, 85, 96, 174

Muscles, 142

Music, 21, 41, 66, 100–103, 191

Music videos, 102, 167

Muslims, 76, 77

Muzak, 101

Nails, 105

Nanny schools, 7

Narcissism, 160–63

NASA, 136

National Archives, 46, 65

National Geographic, 44

National Guard, 101

National parks, 143, 193

National security, 164

Native Americans, 149

NATO, 61–62, 70

Nature Valley Granola, Fruit and Nuts, 183

Navajo, 202

Navy, U.S., 58, 59–60

"NBC Nightly News," 94

Nearsightedness, 7

Nebraska, 43

Neo-Nazis, 55–56

Net worth, 112, 116, 130

Neuharth, Al, 104

Nevada, 20, 149

New England, 21, 88

New Hampshire, 149

New Jersey, 185

New Kids on the Block, 102

New Orleans, La., 88

News, 93–95

Newspapers, 35, 93, 94, 104, 194

New York City, 4, 5, 18, 23, 35, 38, 45, 55, 85–87, 94, 107, 112, 127, 130, 137, 142, 144, 146, 150, 153, 154, 159, 160, 164, 168, 182, 184, 185, 191, 196, 203

New York City Ballet, 191

New York State, 143, 145

New York Stock Exchange, 121

New York Times, 42, 53, 54, 94, 95, 171, 182

New York Transit Authority, 87

Niagara Falls, 44, 201

Nicaragua, 16, 63, 72, 73, 74, 81, 118

"Nightline," 77, 93–94

Nightmares, 200

1984, 103

Nintendo, 199

Nixon, Richard M., 46, 65, 130

Noriega, Manuel, 41–42, 52

North, Oliver, 23

North Carolina, 150

North Dakota, 89

Northeast, 21, 119

Norwood, Jennifer, 102

Nostradamus, 164

Novack, Brian, 161

Nuclear reactors, 145

Nuclear weapons, 61, 70, 164

Nudity, 179, 200, 202

Numerology, 166

INDEX

INDEX

INDEX

INDEX

INDEX

INDEX

INDEX